The Mirror CLASSIC CARTOON COLLECTION

PREMIERE EDITION
Compiled by Mike Higgs

**THE MIRROR
CLASSIC CARTOON
COLLECTION**

PREMIERE EDITION

ISBN 1 899441 75 1

Published by
HAWK BOOKS
P.O. Box 30
Penryn
Cornwall TR10 9YP

Cartoons Copyright © 1998
Mirror Group Newspapers Ltd.

*MGN Ltd. has asserted its right to be
identified as Author of this work.*

This arrangement copyright © 1998
Hawk Books.

Printed and bound in Great Britain by
Butler & Tanner Ltd, Frome and London

The Mirror CLASSIC CARTOON COLLECTION

CONTENTS

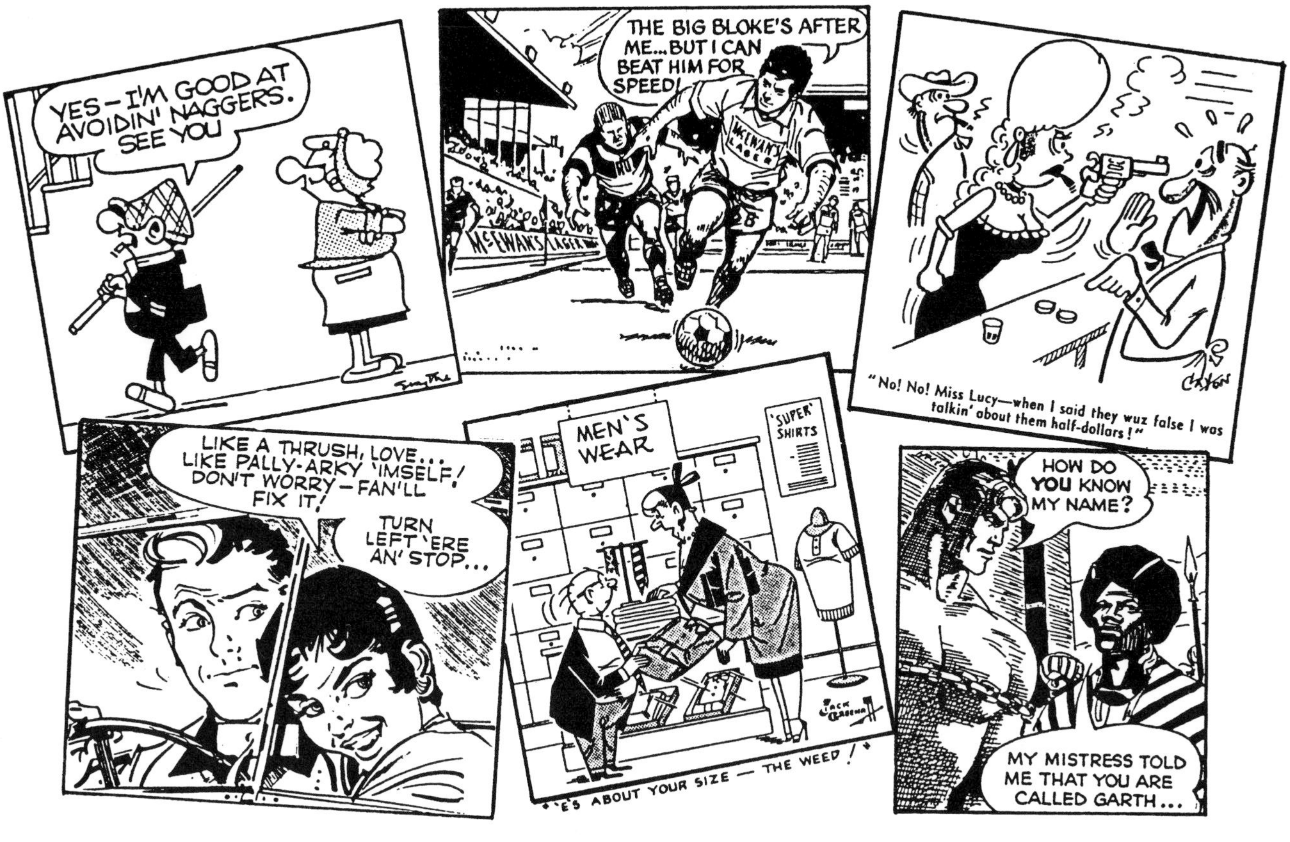

Introduction

'Every picture tells a story', so the saying goes and the cartoon pictures in the Mirror have certainly proved that saying to be a true one. They have been telling a wide variety of stories for decades. In times of war, peace, recession or celebration, the cartoon features have provided a steady diet of humour, adventure and social comment that has entertained millions of readers on a daily basis. Many of the characters that populate these paper plays have become household names and even the lesser known ones have always managed to gather a following of fans at least as devoted as those of any guitar-plucking pop star.

This book is hopefully the first in a short series of volumes that will celebrate the many classic cartoon features that have appeared in the Mirror over the years and will provide a lasting record of a large cast of fictional characters that have entertained so many for so long, not to mention being an interesting and unique social document in it's own right, worthy of any collector's bookshelf.

As a cartoonist myself, I felt particularly pleased when I had the chance to become, for a while, part of the privileged list of contributors to the Mirror's legendary catalogue of cartoon features and I would like to dedicate this book to all the other artists and writers, past and present, who can lay claim to being part of that list.

Mike Higgs
(Creator: Baz & Co. 1991-93)

Garth

'Garth' is probably the best known of the Mirror's action adventure strip characters. He started his long career travelling backwards and forwards in time and space in July 1943. The artist that originated his adventures was Steve Dowling who also created the look of several other classic Mirror strips during his time behind the drawing board. On Dowling's retirement in 1969, the strip was continued for a couple of years by John Allard until a new artist was signed who changed the look of the strip completely. Before we look at the change of style further on in this volume, let's enjoy a story from 1957 by the original artist.

THE NIGHT IS WARM AND STIFLING... GARTH PLUNGES INTO THE LAKE NEAR HIS LITTLE CAMP IN THE LONELY HILLS...

BUT HE IS NOT UNOBSERVED!...

AHH... THAT FEELS BETTER...

WHAT THE DEVIL IS *THAT*?

IT'S A... A GREAT TRANSPARENT SPHERE! AND IT'S MOVING TOWARDS ME!

GARTH MOVES FROM THE SPHERE'S PATH, BUT IT VEERS TO FOLLOW HIM, ROLLING SMOOTHLY AND SILENTLY OVER THE ROUGH GROUND...

NO SENSE IN TAKING CHANCES! I'M NOT GOING TO LET IT GET TOO CLOSE!

I DON'T KNOW WHAT IT *IS*... BUT IF IT KEEPS COMING AT ME I'LL TAKE A SLAM AT IT!

THE MONSTROUS SPHERE FLOWS STRAIGHT AT GARTH...AND HE STRIKES HARD!

UHH!

THERE'S NO SUBSTANCE TO IT!- IT'S LIKE HITTING THE AIR!

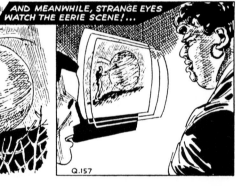

AND MEANWHILE, STRANGE EYES WATCH THE EERIE SCENE!...

IT ISN'T... *SOLID!* (GASP)... I CAN'T DAMAGE IT! *CAN'T* STOP IT!

AHH!

AS GARTH FALLS, THE SPHERE ROLLS ON!...ITS YIELDING MASS ENGULFS HIM, AND IN THE SAME MOMENT HIS MIND BLACKS OUT...

GARTH DOES NOT KNOW HOW LONG HAS PASSED WHEN HIS SENSES SLOWLY RETURN...

HEY, WAKE UP, MAN!- GARTH, HUH? QUEER NAME! HUR-HUR-HUR! BUT NEVER MIND! HOW ARE YOU FEELING, FELLOW?

WE SAW YOU TRYING TO FIGHT THAT SNATCHER! HA-HA-HAA! WATCHED IT ON THE SCREEN

THE *SNATCHER?* THAT SPHERE OF... *NOTHING* THAT SWALLOWED ME UP?

SURE! IT'S A FORCE-FIELD OR SOMETHING - I WOULDN'T KNOW WHAT! LOOKED PRETTY FUNNY, DIDN'T HE, KLUM?

HUMOUR IS AN EMOTION, AND I HAVE NO EMOTIONS, MASTER

LOOK, HAREK... I'VE GOT A LOT OF QUESTIONS TO ASK *YOU*!

DON'T CROWD ME, BOY! LET'S KEEP IT FRIENDLY!

WE ARE APPROACHING THE CO-ORDINATES FOR THE GALAXY-JUMP, MASTER!

ALL RIGHT, KLUM... WE'LL GO AND GET SNUGGED DOWN – MAILA, YOU TAKE CARE OF THE BIG FELLER

I'LL *LIKE* THAT...

Q.170

WHERE DOES YOUR HOME PLANET LIE?

IN ANOTHER GALAXY, GARTH

IN...ANOTHER... *GALAXY*! – BUT THAT MEANS IT'S MILLIONS OF LIGHT-YEARS AWAY!

AT THE PROPER CO-ORDINATES, WE SHIFT THROUGH SUB-SPACE TO REACH OUR GALAXY INSTANTANEOUSLY... BUT YOU MUST BE PROTECTED DURING THE SHIFT

AND SO...

YOU'LL HAVE TO SQUEEZE IN WITH ME... *MY*, YOU'VE GOT MUSCLES! I'LL BET YOU'RE PRETTY NEAR HALF AS STRONG AS KLUM!

Q.171

THERE'S A KIND OF SOMETHING IN THESE PROTECTION-CHAMBERS THAT STOPS US COMING APART AT THE SEAMS DURING THE GALAXY-JUMP... SEE?

Q.172

ABRUPTLY GARTH FEELS A STRANGE SENSATION BATTERING AT HIS BODY!

HERE WE GO...

AH...WE'RE THROUGH NOW...

WHY DIDN'T KLUM HAVE TO BE PROTECTED?

KLUM? *HUK-HUK-HUK*! HE'S NOT ONE OF *US*! HE'S NOT EVEN ONE OF *YOU*, FELLER!

WE'LL BE LANDING SOON... LET'S ALL HAVE A DRINK

NOT FOR ME

Q.173

WELL...THAT HE'S JUST A *DOLL*, OF COURSE! DON'T YOU HAVE DOLLS ON YOUR PLANET?

WHAT DID YOU MEAN WHEN YOU SAID KLUM ISN'T ONE OF *US*?

HEY, KLUM! COME THROUGH AND EXPLAIN YOURSELF! – HA-HA-*HAR*!

A... *DOLL*?

MAILA SAYS YOU'RE A...A *DOLL*, KLUM! WHAT DOES SHE MEAN?

IT IS A SLANG WORD, GARTH...

Q.174

SHE MEANS THAT I AM AN ANDROID... A ROBOT MADE IN THE LIKENESS OF A HUMAN BEING

WHAT?

DON'T JUST *TELL* HIM! – SHOW HIM YOUR MUSCLES, KLUM!

HUK-HUK-HUK! THAT'S GOOD!

OBEDIENTLY KLUM TOUCHES A STUD ON HIS BELT... AND A PANEL OPENS ACROSS HIS CHEST

GARTH

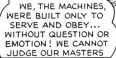

14

WHAT'S PUZZLING YOU *NOW*, FELLER?

A LOT!... BUT MAINLY *WHY* YOU SHOULD CROSS SPACE TO BRING *ME* BACK TO A... A *PARTY* OF ALL THINGS!

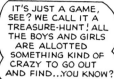

IT'S JUST A GAME, SEE? WE CALL IT A TREASURE-HUNT! ALL THE BOYS AND GIRLS ARE ALLOTTED SOMETHING KIND OF CRAZY TO GO OUT AND FIND...YOU KNOW?

UMM..! THEY HAVE A SIMILAR SORT OF PARTY-GAME ON MY OWN WORLD, BUT IT'S MORE ...LIMITED!

Q.180

HA-*HAR*!... HE'S DROLL, EH, MAILA? THE GANG'LL JUST LOVE HIM!

THE ELEVATOR WHISKS GARTH AND HIS STRANGE COMPANIONS UP FROM THE UNDERGROUND HANGAR...

...SO IN THIS TREASURE-HUNT GAME, HAREK AND I DREW THE JOB OF BRINGING BACK A NATIVE FROM SOME LITTLE DUMP CALLED...ER, *WHAT* WAS IT AGAIN?

WE CALL IT...'*EARTH*', MAILA

I'M TELLING YOU, BOY...KLUM WAS REAL SMART JUST *FINDING* YOUR PLANET! Q.181

HI, PEOPLE! IT'S YOUR GENIAL HOST HIMSELF!– HUK-HUK-HUK!

BRING HIM ALONG, MAILA!

WHAT WAS IT HAREK AND MAILA HAD TO GET IN THE TREASURE HUNT?

I FORGET ... BUT IT *COULDN'T* HAVE BEEN WORSE THAN OURS...

...*WE* HAD TO GET THE TOOTH OF A '*SKARL*' FROM SOME FRIGHTFUL PRE-HUMAN PLANET! LOST TWO ANDROIDS AND A ROBO-TANK IN GETTING IT!

FRIENDS...THIS IS GARTH! PICKED HIM UP ON *TALA*... OR *EARTH* AS HE CALLS IT!

WONDER IF HE'S HAD OUR LANGUAGE TAPED IN! LET'S GO AND SEE!

Q.182

YOU LIKE PRETTY BEADS, HUH?

Q.183

I'M NOT INTERESTED IN BEADS...NOR IN BRAINLESS FOOLS WHO NEITHER WORK NOR THINK! WHO ARE *HELPLESS* WITHOUT THE ANDROIDS AND ROBOTS THEIR FOREFATHERS BUILT!

YOU'VE HAD YOUR FUN, HAREK! WHEN DO I GO BACK TO EARTH?

HA-HA-*HAR*! ISN'T HE GREAT?

GO ON, HAREK... MAKE HIM SAY SOME MORE FUNNY THINGS!

HAVE HIM TELL US ABOUT *HIS* PLANET, HAREK... THAT SHOULD BE GOOD FOR A LAUGH!

Q.184

I'D RATHER TELL YOUR ANDROIDS!– *YOU* WOULDN'T HAVE THE BRAINS TO KNOW WHAT I WAS TALKING ABOUT!

BY THUNDER, I'D LIKE TO KNOCK A FEW HEADS TOGETHER!– BUT IT WOULDN'T GET ME ANYWHERE...

I NEED TIME TO THINK...

HE'S GOT A *NERVE*! A CLOWN FROM SOME DIRTY LITTLE PRIMITIVE PLANET, AND HE ACTS LIKE HE WAS BETTER THAN *US*!

'MMM... HE'S BEGINNING TO GET *ME* KIND OF SORE...

THOSE TWO OVER THERE BEING BADGERED BY THAT LITTLE CROWD...

THEY'RE *DIFFERENT* FROM THE REST... *AND* FROM EACH OTHER! — WONDER IF THEY'VE BEEN SNATCHED OFF OTHER PLANETS BY THIS CRAZY CREW, JUST AS I WAS?

HEY, SHORTY! TELL US ABOUT THE MARVELS OF SCIENCE ON *YOUR* WORLD! HAVE YOU GOT AS FAR AS THE STEAM-ENGINE YET? HA-HA-HA!

WE ARE USING APPLIED ATOMIC THEORY...

DON'T ANSWER THE MOCKING FOOLS!

AH! YOU GOT BACK WITH *YOUR* CRITTUR THEN, HAREK? HA-HA-HA! HAVE HIM COME AND MEET THESE TWO! HAS HE BEEN HYPNO-TAPED TO TALK OUR LANGUAGE?

HE TALKS ALL RIGHT... AND HE'S BEGINNING TO TALK OUT OF TURN!

MY NAME IS GARTH... FROM A PLANET CALLED EARTH

WE, ALSO, HAVE BEEN TAKEN FROM OUR DIFFERENT WORLDS BY THESE PEOPLE... I AM ROGAN, FROM CIRESTES

BRON... FROM LYRGA

BRING GARTH AND THE OTHER TWO, HAREK! WE'RE GOING TO HAVE SOME FUN WITH THEM!

WE'LL SET THEM GOING ON A *DRINKING CONTEST!* THERE'S NOTHING LIKE A DRUNK ALIEN FOR LAUGHS!

I'LL LAY ODDS THAT GARTH'S THE LAST TO GO UNDER! ANY TAKERS?

I AM NO *ANIMAL* FOR THESE FOOLS TO SPORT WITH! I WILL FLING THEIR VILE LIQUOR IN THEIR FACES!

LET US BE PRUDENT, MY FRIENDS —

PRUDENT, HELL! I'M SICK OF THIS!

QUIET, FOLKS! THE BIG DRINKING MATCH IS ON! THEY DRINK LEVEL, AND THE LAST ONE ON HIS FEET IS THE WINNER!

HA-HA-HA!

ABRUPTLY GARTH'S TEMPER SNAPS

DRINK IT YOURSELF!

CRASH

ALL RIGHT... ALL *RIGHT!* I'LL SHOW THAT SMART APE WHAT'S WHAT! STAND BACK, EVERYBODY! I'M GOING TO HAVE ONE OF THE DOLLS TAKE HIM APART!

HAREK!

AT HAREK'S ORDER, ONE OF THE ANDROIDS MOVES FORWARD...

YOU ASKED FOR IT, GARTH — ALL RIGHT, SHEK... *BREAK HIM UP!*

I HEAR YOU, MASTER

WAIT! YOUR ANDROIDS ARE MANY TIMES STRONGER THAN ANY HUMAN! *I* WILL FIGHT BESIDE GARTH!

THANKS, BRON... BUT I THINK I CAN HANDLE IT!

BY THE TWIN MOONS OF LYRGA! THIS GARTH IS OF A FIGHTING BREED! A MAN AFTER MY OWN HEART!

IF HE RECKONS HE CAN BEAT A DOLL, HE'S *CRAZY!*

THE ANDROID, A THING OF METAL AND PLASTIC WITH SUPERHUMAN STRENGTH, MOVES IN TO CRUSH GARTH... AND IS THROWN!

HOW THE -?

GASP!

THUD!

I AM A MAN OF LEARNING, NOT OF VIOLENCE ...BUT IT SEEMS TO ME THAT OUR FRIEND IS EMPLOYING A MOST *SCIENTIFIC* METHOD OF COMBAT!

HE'S GOOD, ROGAN ...*VERY* GOOD! I'VE SEEN PLENTY, AND I *KNOW*!

NOW WATCH HIM...HE'S GOT TO KEEP THROWING THAT DOLL *WITHOUT EVER LETTING IT GET A GRIP ON HIM!*...

Q.190

THE ANDROID MOVES IN ON GARTH ...

I'LL SEND THAT DOLL FOR SCRAP IF IT DOESN'T FINISH GARTH OFF DAMN QUICK!

YOU KNOW, I SORT OF TOOK TO GARTH - I'LL BE SORRY TO SEE HIM KILLED...

Q.191

SAVE YOUR REGRETS, WOMAN! THE ANDROID IS STRONGER, BUT IT HAS NO INSTINCT FOR THE TRICKS OF BALANCE AND LEVERAGE THAT A FIGHTING MAN UNDERSTANDS! YOU WILL SEE -

OUR FRIEND IS DOWN, BRON!

SHEK'S *GOT HIM*! HUK-HUK-HUK! YOU *STILL* THINK GARTH CAN WIN, BOY?

CACKLE, GREAT FOOL! GARTH HAS FALLEN ONLY TO GAIN THE ADVANTAGE !... WATCH NOW...

Q.192

GARTH ROLLS BACKWARDS AND THRUSTS WITH ALL THE FORCE OF HIS POWERFUL LEGS...

HA!

THUD!

GASP!

THE DOLL'S *WRECKED!* - FINISHED! - I... I CAN'T BELIEVE IT!

A FINE THROW, GARTH !...

YOU FOUGHT THAT MACHINE THE ONLY WAY POSSIBLE !... BUT TELL ME NOW, ON *YOUR* WORLD, DO YOU USE THE CLENCHED-FIST METHOD OF COMBAT ?...

...LIKE THIS !

CRACK!

Q.193

THAT WAS UNWISE, BRON !... OUR ONE HOPE OF BEING RETURNED TO OUR OWN WORLDS IS TO PLACATE THESE PEOPLE...

THEY'VE TURNED DANGEROUS! GET THE DOLLS *QUICK!*

YOU MAY BE RIGHT, ROGAN, BUT IT'S TOO LATE NOW !...SO LET'S MAKE THE BEST OF THINGS THE WAY THEY ARE !

Q.194

HAVE THOSE ANDROIDS KEEP BACK, OR YOUR FRIEND HAREK GOES OVER THE EDGE!

HOLD IT, YOU DOLLS!

17

YOU'VE STOPPED THEM, GARTH! CAN WE MAKE THESE PEOPLE ORDER THEIR ANDROIDS TO TAKE US BACK TO OUR OWN PLANETS?

A WILD HOPE, BRON— BUT WE HAVE NOTHING TO LOSE BY TRYING—

Q.195

MAILA!...WHAT CAN WE DO?

THERE'S NO NEED FOR US TO DO ANYTHING, EVEN IF WE COULD! I'LL JUST HAVE THE WATCH-DOG TAKE OVER

SOMEWHERE AN ALARM-IMPULSE REGISTERS... A GIANT POSITRONIC BRAIN SCANS THE SCENE AND ASSESSES IT, THEN PREPARES TO SAVE ITS MASTER...

Q.196

WE'LL TRY TO GET DOWN TO THE SPACE-SHIP HANGARS! READY, YOU TWO?...

GET THAT ELEVATOR GOING, ROGAN! IF WE CAN MAKE HAREK GIVE HIS ANDROIDS THE RIGHT ORDERS, WE'LL BE AWAY!

DON'T WORRY, HAREK!— THE WATCH-DOG HAS TAKEN OVER!— IT'LL SOON PUT THOSE CRITTURS WHERE THEY BELONG!

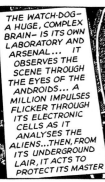

THE WATCH-DOG— A HUGE, COMPLEX BRAIN— IS ITS OWN LABORATORY AND ARSENAL... IT OBSERVES THE SCENE THROUGH THE EYES OF THE ANDROIDS... A MILLION IMPULSES FLICKER THROUGH ITS ELECTRONIC CELLS AS IT ANALYSES THE ALIENS...THEN, FROM ITS UNDERGROUND LAIR, IT ACTS TO PROTECT ITS MASTER

SMALL SPHERES OF LIGHT, CRACKLING WITH POWER, DART FROM HIDDEN VENTS AND ARE GUIDED TOWARDS THEIR TARGETS...

THE ELEVATOR'S READY, GARTH!

LOOK OUT!

Q.197

A FORCE-SPHERE TOUCHES BRON'S HEAD... AND VANISHES, FELLING HIM LIKE A MAN STRUCK BY LIGHTNING!

BRON!

Q.198

GARTH AND ROGAN FALL ALSO...

UHH...

POOR HAREK ...DID HE HURT YOU?

CRAZY, DUMB NATIVES! ARE THEY DEAD?

NO, MASTER!... NOT KNOWING YOUR WISHES, THE WATCH-DOG ACTED ONLY TO STUN THEM!

ROGAN! ...WHERE ARE WE? ...WHAT HAPPENED?

Q.199

AH! YOU HAVE RECOVERED!— BRON IS ALSO ALIVE, AND WILL SOON COME TO HIS SENSES, I THINK

I AWOKE TO FIND THAT WE WERE IN THIS CHAMBER, WHICH SEEMS TO BE SOME SORT OF PRISON OR CELL

I HAVE BEEN TRYING TO FIND THE DOOR, BUT WITHOUT SUCCESS... IT IS VERY CLEVERLY CONCEALED

WAKE UP, BRON — WAKE UP!

COME ON, BRON!

STRANGE THAT *I* SHOULD BE THE FIRST TO RECOVER... IT COULD BE A MATTER OF METABOLISM, OR—

ARE YOU A SCIENTIST, ROGAN?

YES! BUT HOW DID YOU KNOW?—DOES YOUR RACE POSSESS RUDIMENTARY POWERS OF TELEPATHY?

MAYBE IT'S JUST THAT YOU REMIND ME OF A FRIEND OF MINE... A SCIENTIST...

ROGAN'S LIKE OLD PROF LUMIERE... PUZZLING OVER SOME ABSTRACT PROBLEM AND FORGETTING WE'RE IN *DANGER*...

Q.200

LET US POOL WHAT LITTLE KNOWLEDGE WE HAVE CONCERNING OUR CAPTORS...

ALL *I* KNOW ABOUT THEM IS THEY'RE *CRAZY*!

I'VE GATHERED THAT THEY WERE A FINE RACE A FEW CENTURIES BACK... BUT HAVING A PRESS-BUTTON WORLD SEEMS TO HAVE MADE THEM GO TO SEED...

NOBODY WORKS, NOBODY THINKS! THE ANDROIDS AND ROBOTS DO *EVERYTHING*! SO THE PEOPLE ACT LIKE A BUNCH OF KIDS AT AN EVERLASTING PARTY...ONLY THEY'RE FAR MORE DANGEROUS!

Q.201

HAREK!

WELL, YOU CRITTURS! I JUST LOOKED IN TO TELL YOU THE BAD NEWS!

STEADY, BRON! YOU CAN'T GET AT HIM!

IT IS ONLY A THREE-DIMENSIONAL IMAGE...

HAR-HA!– YOU FELLOWS ARE BEGINNING TO GET SMART!

Q.202

TOO BAD IT CAN'T LAST, THOUGH!

WE'VE THOUGHT UP A GREAT STUNT SO YOU CAN ENTERTAIN US TOMORROW! BEST FUN WE'VE HAD FOR A LONG TIME!— IT'LL *SLAY* YOU! HUK-HUK-HUK!

TOMORROW WE'LL GIVE EACH OF YOU CRITTURS A PRIMITIVE WEAPON FROM MY MUSEUM, SEE? AND THEN YOU ENTERTAIN US WITH A THREE-CORNERED FIGHT...TO A FINISH!

Q.203

DOES THE FOOL THINK HE CAN *MAKE* US FIGHT?

I'VE GOT *THAT* FIGURED, BOY! LAST ONE LEFT ALIVE GETS A FREE TRIP HOME! THINK IT OVER! HUK-HUK-HUK!

THE IMAGE OF HAREK VANISHES, AND THE ECHOES OF HIS JEERING LAUGHTER FADE AWAY...

HOME...

SO ONE OF US MUST KILL THE OTHER TWO TO GET BACK HOME! *YOU'RE* IN LUCK, GARTH!

DON'T BE A COUPLE OF FOOLS...WE STICK TOGETHER! IF I KILL ANYBODY, IT'LL BE HAREK

AHH...

WE HONOUR YOU FOR THIS, GARTH– YOU WOULD SURELY HAVE WON...

ENOUGH, ROGAN!– HIS BREED WANTS NO PRAISE!–HE IS A MAN, AND HAS DONE WHAT HE MUST!

THANKS, BRON...NOW LET'S GET ON WITH OUR COUNCIL OF WAR! TOMORROW MAY OFFER A CHANCE TO ESCAPE...AND WE *MUST* BE READY TO EXPLOIT IT!

Q.204

DOES ANYBODY KNOW WHAT THINGS ARE LIKE HERE ON URGON... OUTSIDE THIS PLACE OF HAREK'S?

WE HAVE GATHERED A FEW FACTS FROM OUR CAPTORS...

IT SEEMS THAT THE POPULATION IS NOT LARGE, BUT GREAT NUMBERS OF ANDROIDS AND ROBOTS WORK CONSTANTLY TO SUPPLY THE DEMANDS OF THEIR MASTERS

AND *CENTRAL CAPITAL* IS THE ONLY CITY ON THE PLANET! MOST PEOPLE HAVE HUGE DOMAINS... LIKE *THIS* ONE, SURROUNDED BY WILD COUNTRY

GOOD! IF WE CAN GET INTO THE WILDS, IT OUGHT TO HELP 'PRIMITIVE CRITTURS' LIKE US TO GIVE HAREK A RUN FOR HIS MONEY!

THE GOVERNMENT OF URGON MUST LIE IN CENTRAL CAPITAL ... AND THEY CAN HARDLY UPHOLD THE RECKLESS ACTIVITIES OF A MAN LIKE HAREK

WE'LL HAVE TO HOPE YOU'RE RIGHT, ROGAN ...

...AND THAT MEANS WE'VE GOT TO FIND OUR WAY TO CENTRAL CAPITAL

WE MAY HAVE TO TREK ACROSS HALF THE PLANET!

LET'S WORRY ABOUT THAT LATER! THE FIRST JOB IS TO BREAK OUT OF HERE...

GET UP ON MY SHOULDERS, BRON

I'M PRETTY SURE THOSE FRETTED PANELS COVER VENTILATOR SHAFTS! CAN YOU PRISE ONE AWAY, BRON?

YES ...AND YOU'RE RIGHT!

THERE'S AN AIR-SHAFT— BUT IT'S TOO NARROW FOR ME TO CRAWL ALONG IT

LACK OF SIZE IS SOMETIMES AN ADVANTAGE! LIFT ME UP, GARTH!

IF YOU CAN FIND A WAY OUT OF THE SHAFT, TRY TO LOCATE THE DOOR OF THIS CHAMBER AND OPEN IT FROM THE OUTSIDE!

ROGAN EDGES HIS WAY ALONG THE CURVING SHAFT FOR SOME DISTANCE...

AH...! THAT GRILLE MAY OFFER A WAY OUT!

A STORE-ROOM OR WORK-SHOP OF SOME KIND... BUT IT SEEMS TO HAVE FALLEN INTO DISUSE...

AND MEANWHILE...

HOPE ROGAN DOESN'T STRIKE TROUBLE – I *LIKE* THAT LITTLE MAN

SO DO I... HE'S GOT A COOL HEAD AND PLENTY OF GUTS

THE NIGHT HOURS PASS, AND STILL ROGAN HAS NOT RETURNED...

HE'S BEEN CAUGHT, GARTH... HE *MUST* HAVE BEEN!

I'M NOT SO SURE...

IF THEY'D CAUGHT HIM, THEY'D HAVE PAID US A VISIT TO FIND OUT HOW HE ESCAPED...AND TO MAKE SURE THAT WE ARE STILL HERE

IN THE DISUSED WORKSHOP, ROGAN IS HAPPILY EMPLOYED...

FASCINATING... QUITE FASCINATING TO WORK WITH SUCH INSTRUMENTS...NOW LET ME SEE... H'MM... YES...

ROGAN! WHERE THE DEVIL HAVE YOU BEEN? IT MUST BE WELL PAST DAWN!

PATIENCE, MY FRIEND... I WILL EXPLAIN HOW I HAVE BEEN AMUSING MYSELF!...

THE ONLY WAY OUT OF THE SHAFT LED TO A DISUSED WORKSHOP... BUT I COULD FIND NO WAY TO OPEN THE DOORS

SO YOU'VE BEEN IN THE WORKSHOP ALL THIS TIME!

Q.210

YES, GARTH... AND THOUGH MUCH OF THE MATERIAL THERE WAS BEYOND MY UNDERSTANDING, SOME OF IT WAS FAMILIAR TO ME...

SO FROM VARIOUS ODDS AND ENDS, I HAVE MADE THIS!

WHAT IS THAT GADGET YOU'VE MADE, ROGAN?

AN OSCILLATOR! IT EMITS A VERY STRONG SIGNAL AT A RANGE JUST ABOVE AUDIO-FREQUENCY

I HOPE IT MAY HELP US TO ESCAPE WHEN WE ARE TAKEN OUT INTO THE OPEN FOR OUR BATTLE!

ONE OF THE PANELS MOVES SILENTLY BACK, AND THREE ANDROIDS APPEAR

YOU WILL COME WITH US—OUR MASTER HAS ORDERED US TO STUN YOU IF YOU SHOW VIOLENCE!

WELL... IT SEEMS HAREK AND HIS CROWD ARE READY TO BE ENTERTAINED BY A LITTLE BLOOD-LETTING!

Q.211

NOW DON'T BE SCARED, BOYS AND GIRLS! I'VE HAD THE DOLLS FIX UP THIS FORCE-BARRIER, SO THAT THE CRITTURS CAN'T GET AT US!

GUARDED BY ANDROIDS AND SEATED IN A STRANGE VEHICLE, GARTH AND HIS FRIENDS ARE BROUGHT TO THE SURFACE...

Q.212

THIS THING WOULD TRAVEL OVER ANY TERRAIN! YOU'RE A TECHNICIAN, BRON— DO YOU THINK YOU COULD OPERATE IT?

I DON'T KNOW HOW IT WORKS, BUT I'VE BEEN WATCHING THE WAY IT'S CONTROLLED, AND THERE'S NOTHING TO IT!

THAT OSCILLATOR YOU MADE, ROGAN... HOW CAN IT HELP US?

THE SIGNAL IS TOO HIGH FOR HUMAN EARS TO HEAR ...BUT NOT, I HOPE, FOR THE SENSITIVE HEARING MECHANISM OF THE ANDROIDS!

SO WHEN I SWITCH ON, I BELIEVE IT WILL IMMOBILISE THE ANDROIDS! THEY HAVE NO INITIATIVE, BUT ACT ONLY ON THEIR MASTER'S COMMAND...

Q.213

...AND IF HAREK'S WORDS ARE BLOTTED OUT BY A SHRILL, CONTINUOUS OSCILLATION...

GIVE THEM THE WEAPONS, YOU DOLLS!

Q.214

MAKE IT GOOD, FELLERS! REMEMBER— THE ONE THAT'S LEFT ALIVE GETS TAKEN BACK TO HIS HOME PLANET!

GARTH WILL WIN... BUT WILL YOU REALLY SEND HIM HOME, HAREK? I THOUGHT YOU WANTED TO KILL HIM!

SURE I'LL SEND HIM HOME! BUT I DIDN'T SAY HE'D GET THERE ALIVE, DID I?— HA-HA-HAR!

23

THROUGHOUT THE DAY, GARTH AND HIS FRIENDS MOVE STEADILY ON THROUGH THE WILDS OF URGON...

IT'LL SOON BE DUSK...WHEN DO WE EAT? AND *WHAT* DO WE EAT?

TRY THIS FRUIT, BRON

UMM... LOOKS ALL RIGHT...

WE'LL CAMP HERE TONIGHT – I'LL TRY THE RIVER FOR FISH ...*THEY* OUGHT TO MAKE SAFE EATING

FISH!..YES, INDEED... I WISH I HAD THOUGHT OF THAT BEFORE EXPERIMENTING WITH OTHER THINGS...

EXPERIMENTING?

HOW DO YOU KNOW THIS FRUIT YOU GAVE ME WAS ALL RIGHT TO EAT, ROGAN?

I DO *NOT* KNOW, MY FRIEND

IF YOU SURVIVE, WE SHALL *THEN* KNOW THAT WE CAN EAT SUCH FRUIT! I MYSELF HAVE EATEN SOME QUITE TASTY TUBERS, AND THE SAME THING APPLIES

TRIAL AND ERROR IS OUR ONLY METHOD, I FEAR

WELL, *THANKS*, PAL!

SPLASH!

WHAT A CHARACTER! I ONLY HOPE THOSE TUBERS DON'T KILL HIM! I'D REALLY MISS THAT LITTLE MAN!

...INTERESTING TO THINK THAT WE HAVE *NO EXPERIENCE WHATEVER* TO TELL US WHAT IS SAFE AND WHAT MAY BE DANGEROUS ON THIS ALIEN WORLD...

IT IS QUITE UNCANNY, THIS FEELING OF TOTAL IGNORANCE

WE HAVE TO LEARN *FAST* IF WE'RE GOING TO GET THROUGH TO CENTRAL CAPITAL!

HEY! SUPPOSE THE RULERS OF THIS CRAZY PLANET ARE NO BETTER THAN HAREK AND HIS FRIENDS! WE'LL BE STUCK HERE ON URGON *FOR LIFE!*

IF THEY ARE ALL LIKE HAREK, WE SHALL NOT LIVE LONG ENOUGH TO BECOME UNDULY HOMESICK, BRON!

THE DAYS HAVE BECOME WEEKS ...AND SOMEHOW THE FUGITIVES SURVIVE THE MANY HAZARDS THAT BESET THEM IN THEIR LONG JOURNEY THROUGH THE WILDS OF THIS UNKNOWN PLANET...

YOU KNOW, ROGAN, I FEEL LIKE AN OLD CAMPAIGNER *NOW*...

WHEN I THINK JUST HOW MUCH WE *DIDN'T* KNOW WHEN WE STARTED THIS TREK, I WONDER WE'RE STILL ALIVE!

IT IS MAINLY THANKS TO GARTH...

THE EARTHMAN IS AN EXPERT IN THE ART OF SURVIVAL!

GARTH AND HIS FRIENDS HAVE PUT ALMOST A THOUSAND LONG, WEARY MILES BEHIND THEM...BUT NOW...

SWAMPLAND!...A HUGE, WATERY SWAMP STRETCHING TO THE HORIZON!

IT MAY TAKE WEEKS...MONTHS TO FIND OUR WAY AROUND THIS...

LOOK AT THE SIZE OF THESE LEAVES! THEY'RE AS BIG AS A SMALL BOAT!

KEEP AWAY FROM THEM, BRON!

26

Q.240

ON THE HIDDEN ISLAND IN THE SWAMP, GARTH AND HIS FRIENDS DESCEND FROM THE GREAT ROBOT

BUILDINGS! ...ROBOTS!... ANDROIDS!

AND *PEOPLE*! THERE'S A WHOLE COMMUNITY HERE!

WE WELCOME YOU, STRANGERS FROM OTHER WORLDS!

YOU ARE SAFE HERE WITH US

I AM SOLAN, AND THIS IS MY WIFE, TARA

WHO ARE YOU? WHAT *IS* THIS COMMUNITY?

HERE, ON THIS ISLAND, YOU ARE AMONG THE OUTCASTS OF OUR CIVILISATION! THEY CALL US... *THE THINKERS*!

Q.241

YE-E-S — THAT MAKES SENSE! HAREK AND HIS CROWD USED THE WORD 'THINKER' AS AN INSULT!

IT WAS PLAIN THAT THEY HAD ONLY CONTEMPT AND HATRED FOR PEOPLE WHO USE THEIR *BRAINS* IN THIS WORLD... WHERE NOBODY NEEDS TO THINK OR WORK!

WE MUST TAKE YOU TO OUR LEADER ... HE IS WAITING TO WELCOME YOU

IT IS NOT FAR...WE COULD GO BY ROBO-CAR, BUT WITH US IT IS A PRINCIPLE *NOT* TO DEPEND ON MACHINES... ONLY TO USE THEM SELECTIVELY!

WE'LL WALK WITH PLEASURE, MA'AM! ...WE *LIKE* THE SYSTEM YOU'VE GOT HERE

Q.242

TO US IT SEEMS YOUR WORLD IS PLAGUED BY ROBOTS!

IT IS LIKE AN ADDICTION ...WE ALONE TRY TO LIVE AS MEN *SHOULD* LIVE...BUT THERE ARE ONLY A FEW THOUSAND OF US!

WE KEEP UP ALL THE BASIC SKILLS THAT HAVE LONG SINCE DIED OUT IN OTHER PARTS OF URGON

Q.243

BUT THOUGH WE LIVE SIMPLY, WE ARE NOT PRIMITIVES! HERE WE DO RESEARCH IN ADVANCE OF ANYTHING THAT THE GREAT ROBO-LABORATORIES OF CENTRAL CAPITAL DO!

WE WERE TRYING TO REACH CENTRAL CAPITAL—HOPING YOUR GOVERNMENT WOULD RETURN US TO OUR OWN WORLDS

THERE IS NO HOPE OF THAT, GARTH ...NONE AT ALL...

THE WORLD COUNCIL OF URGON WOULD NEVER STIR THEMSELVES TO SEND YOU HOME

BUT *YOU*... THE THINKERS ...YOU HAVE SPACE-SHIPS?

NO, GARTH...SPACE IS BARRED TO US, AND ALWAYS WILL BE

Q.244

COME...OUR LEADER WILL EXPLAIN ALL THINGS TO YOU

A DOOR SILENTLY OPENS...

THIS IS OUR LEADER ...KYRON

BE WELCOME, STRANGERS... AND STRIVE TO BE CONTENT HERE, FOR THERE IS NO OTHER REFUGE EXCEPT WITH US

TELL ME YOUR NAMES... AND THE WORLDS WHENCE YOU COME

I AM GARTH... FROM EARTH

BRON, FROM LYRGA

ROGAN, FROM CIRESTES

BEFORE YOU TAKE YOUR PLACE IN OUR COMMUNITY, TO LIVE AND WORK AMONG US, YOU MUST KNOW THE BITTER STORY OF THIS WORLD IN WHICH WE, *THE THINKERS*, ARE OUTCASTS...

WE ARE A RACE WHOSE TECHNICAL SKILL OUTRAN OUR CULTURAL MATURITY...

UH? WHAT DOES *THAT* MEAN?

IT MEANS THEY DEVELOPED A PRESS-BUTTON WORLD WHERE *ROBOTS* DO EVERYTHING ...AND THEN THE PEOPLE WENT TO SEED FROM SHEER WORLD-WIDE *BOREDOM*...

YOU'VE SEEN IT, BRON! THAT WAS THE TROUBLE WITH HAREK AND HIS FRIENDS!

EXCEPT ON THIS ISLAND, IT IS THE SAME THROUGHOUT THE WORLD... *EVEN IN CENTRAL CAPITAL!*

THE ROBOT AGE CAME TOO SUDDENLY...PEOPLE FOUND THEMSELVES IN A WORLD WITHOUT WANT... A WORLD IN WHICH ALL MEN HAD UNTOLD LEISURE...

IN A FEW GENERATIONS OUR WHOLE RACE BECAME SOFT AND DEGENERATE... THERE WAS NO NEED TO WORK, NOR EVEN TO *THINK*...AND ONLY A HANDFUL OF PEOPLE REALISED THE DANGER!...

TO STRIVE FOR FRESH ACHIEVEMENT IS A BASIC HUMAN NEED! TAKE THAT AWAY, AND MAN IS BUT A HOLLOW SHELL, MOULDERING FROM WITHIN...

I HAVE BROUGHT REFRESHMENT FOR OUR FRIENDS, KYRON...YOU ARE TELLING THEM OF THE PAST?

YES, TARA...THEY MUST KNOW OF THAT TO UNDERSTAND THE PRESENT...A WORLD WHERE MEN SEEK ONLY FOR NEW WAYS TO AMUSE THEMSELVES...NEW PLEASURES ...NEW SENSATIONS...

A FRANTIC PURSUIT OF HAPPINESS... YES, WE HAVE SEEN IT AT CLOSE QUARTERS, KYRON!

WE, *THE THINKERS*, ARE HATED AND DESPISED AS AN OUTCAST SECT ...BUT THEY DO NOT TRY TO SEEK US OUT AND DESTROY US, BECAUSE THEY KNOW WE CAN DO THEM NO HARM...

KYRON...YOU ARE THE LEADER OF THE THINKERS...WHAT IS YOUR ULTIMATE PURPOSE?

OUR PURPOSE..?

IT IS SIMPLY *TO EXIST*! TO WORK, AND THINK, AND LIVE AS HUMANS *SHOULD* LIVE! THAT IS ALL... WE CAN DO NO MORE THAN KEEP ALIVE A LITTLE SPARK OF WHAT WAS ONCE THE GREAT FLAME OF OUR HERITAGE

GARTH, BRON AND ROGAN EXCHANGE GLANCES... THEN GARTH SPEAKS FOR THEM ALL!

WE ARE GRATEFUL TO HAVE FOUND REFUGE WITH YOU...BUT WE CAN'T RESIGN OURSELVES TO A LIFETIME HERE! SOMEHOW, WE MEAN TO ESCAPE FROM THIS WORLD!

Q.250 YOU TALK OF ESCAPE ...OF RETURNING TO YOUR OWN WORLD! BUT THAT IS FOOLISH TALK!

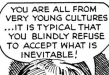

YOU ARE ALL FROM VERY YOUNG CULTURES ...IT IS TYPICAL THAT YOU BLINDLY REFUSE TO ACCEPT WHAT IS INEVITABLE!

WE *DO* REFUSE! ...AND THAT'S WHAT HAS KEPT US ALIVE ON THIS ALIEN PLANET FOR MONTHS

HE IS RIGHT, TARA...THEY COME OF YOUNG RACES...BUT THOUGH YOUTH IS SOMETIMES FOOLISH, IT IS *ALWAYS* DYNAMIC! WE NEED THEIR SPIRIT AMONG US!

THE DAYS PASS SLOWLY FOR GARTH AND HIS FRIENDS, EXILED ON THE ISLAND OF THINKERS...

WHAT ARE YOU MAKING, BRON?

A TOY FOR ONE OF THE CHILDREN ...A MAN MUST DO *SOMETHING* TO SAVE HIMSELF DYING OF BOREDOM

POOR BRON... YOU'ARE AS RESTLESS AS GARTH...

HE IS TEACHING THE CHILDREN SOME STRANGE GAME THAT IS PLAYED ON HIS OWN WORLD WITH A LEATHER SPHERE!

Q.251

YOU HAVE NOT FOUND A WAY TO ESCAPE FROM THIS PLANET YET...AND I FEAR YOU NEVER WILL...BUT AT LEAST YOUR LITTLE FRIEND ROGAN IS ENJOYING HIMSELF

I KNOW... *HE'S* A SCIENTIST...

Q.252

HE SPENDS ALL HIS TIME WITH YOUR OWN SCIENTISTS...IT'S GREAT FOR HIM, EVEN IF HE DOES ONLY UNDERSTAND A QUARTER OF WHAT THEY TELL HIM!

IS THIS *TRUE*, MELCHAR? ABOUT THE CENTRAL SOURCE OF POWER FOR ALL ROBOTS?

BUT OF COURSE, ROGAN!

I MUST TELL GARTH! *AT ONCE!*

THIS WILL INTEREST YOU, GARTH! FIRST, YOU RECALL *WHY* THE THINKERS CANNOT SEND US HOME?

NO SPACE-SHIP! THEY HAVEN'T THE RESOURCES TO BUILD ONE...AND THEY CAN HARDLY APPLY TO CENTRAL CAPITAL FOR ONE

AHH...CENTRAL CAPITAL... THAT IS THE KEY TO OUR PROBLEM! DID YOU KNOW THAT *FROM* CENTRAL CAPITAL RADIATES THE POWER THAT OPERATES EVERY MACHINE ON THIS PLANET OF URGON?

Q 253

WHAT? ROBOTS, ANDROIDS, *EVERYTHING*? IT'S FANTASTIC!

YES...BUT IT IS ALSO *TRUE*! THINK WHAT IT MEANS TO US, GARTH!

UH?...*WHAT* DOES IT MEAN?

YOU WISH TO SPEAK WITH ME, MY FRIENDS?

KYRON...WE HAVE LEARNED THAT EVERY MACHINE ON URGON OPERATES BY POWER RADIATED *FROM A SINGLE SOURCE!*

THAT IS TRUE, GARTH... *THE MASTERS* WORKED FOR TWO CENTURIES TO BUILD THE GREAT SOLAR POWER-HOUSE WHICH GAVE THEIR DESCENDANTS THE USE OF UNLIMITED POWER FOR ALL TIME...

Q. 254

ENERGY IS DRAWN FROM OUR TWIN SUNS, AND RADIATED OVER THE WHOLE PLANET... IN EVERY ROBOT, EVERY ANDROID, EVERY MACHINE, THERE IS A UNIT WHICH PICKS UP THIS RADIATED POWER...AND USES IT AS REQUIRED

IF THIS GREAT SOLAR POWER-HOUSE *FAILED*... WHAT WOULD HAPPEN?

EVERY ANDROID, ROBOT, AND MACHINE IN THE WORLD WOULD CONTINUE TO OPERATE ON STORED POWER... *FOR ABOUT TWELVE HOURS!*

... AND THEN THE WHOLE ROBOT CULTURE OF URGON WOULD RUN DOWN AND STOP...

BUT THERE IS NO DANGER OF FAILURE! *THE MASTERS* BUILT WELL! THE SOLAR POWER-HOUSE IS SELF-MAINTAINING... IT WILL OUTLAST TIME...

NOT IF WE *SABOTAGED* IT!

WHAT?

SABOTAGE THE WORLD'S SOLAR POWER-HOUSE? BUT THAT IS MADNESS!

NO, TARA! IT ONLY SEEMS MADNESS TO YOU BECAUSE YOU'VE ALWAYS LIVED IN A WORLD SERVED BY ROBOTS!... THE IDEA OF EVERYTHING GRINDING TO A HALT MAKES YOU SHUDDER! *YET IT COULD BRING ABOUT WHAT YOU WANT!*

IT COULD, BY SHEER NECESSITY, TURN THIS WORLD OF DRONES INTO A WORLD OF PEOPLE WHO THINK AND WORK ONCE AGAIN

THIS IS A HUGE AND REVOLUTIONARY THOUGHT, BUT WE MUST NOT FLINCH FROM IT... SUMMON THE COUNCIL, TARA!

THE COUNCIL IS IN SESSION...

I SAY THAT TO DESTROY THE SOLAR POWER-HOUSE IS NOT ONLY UNTHINKABLE BUT IMPOSSIBLE!

GARTH DID NOT SUGGEST *DESTROYING* IT... ONLY SABOTAGING IT IN SUCH A WAY THAT IT CAN BE RE-ACTIVATED AGAIN *UNDER THE CONTROL OF THE THINKERS!*

YOUR SCIENTISTS WOULD HAVE TO WORK OUT HOW THAT COULD BEST BE DONE!

WHAT DO *YOU* SAY, MELCHAR?

IT IS TECHNICALLY POSSIBLE... BUT I AM AGAINST IT!

GARTH'S PLAN WILL BRING EVERY MACHINE ON THE PLANET TO A STOP... IT WILL MEAN WORLD-WIDE CATASTROPHE...

WE ALREADY HAVE A WORLD-WIDE CATASTROPHE... A CULTURE THAT IS ROTTEN TO THE CORE! THIS PLAN WILL CAUSE *HARDSHIP*... MEN WILL HAVE TO FEND FOR THEMSELVES AGAIN...

GOOD FOR YOU, SOLAN! MAKE 'EM WORK AND THINK, EH?

BUT THAT IS WHAT THIS WORLD *NEEDS* FOR ITS SALVATION!

YOU HAVE SAID NOTHING YET, KYRON... AND WE LOOK TO YOU AS OUR LEADER

WE'LL ALL ACCEPT YOUR DECISION!

THEN... LET THIS THING BE DONE – IF IT *CAN* BE DONE...

YOU TALK TO THE SCIENTISTS, ROGAN... FIND OUT WHAT YOU THINK WE'LL NEED TO KNOW WHEN WE GET INTO THE POWER-STATION

SOLAN! YOU AND I WILL HAVE A TALK ABOUT *HOW* TO GET INSIDE!

GARTH

31

GARTH

32

IN WITH YOU, BRON! WE'VE ONLY A FEW SECONDS LEFT!

DROP THE HATCH! IF IT SMASHES AGAINST THE ROCK THERE'LL BE AN ALERT IN "DAMAGE CONTROL" AND THE TRUCK MAY BE HALTED!

CLANG

THE HURTLING TRUCK VANISHES INTO THE TWO-MILE TUNNEL LEADING TO THE GREAT SOLAR STATION WHICH PROVIDES POWER FOR THE WHOLE PLANET...

Q.270

WELL...WE'RE ON OUR WAY INTO YOUR *IMPREGNABLE* POWER HOUSE, MELCHAR!

YOU MOCK, BRON...BUT THE MASTERS WHO BUILT IT MADE A VERY NATURAL ERROR OF JUDGMENT...

THEY COULD IMAGINE NO MOTIVE WHICH MIGHT MAKE A MAN WANT TO ENTER ... AND THEY COULD IMAGINE NO MAN WITH THE STRENGTH TO DO WHAT GARTH JUST DID...

Q.271

AH! WE'RE SLOWING TO A HALT...

...AND THE HATCH IS *OPENING*!

OUT NOW! QUICKLY!

THE TRUCK WILL PASS UNDER A HOPPER TO BE FILLED WITH ONE OF THE BY-PRODUCTS OF THE POWER HOUSE...

NOW IT BEGINS! THIS PLACE IS AS BIG AS A DOMAIN... AND IN IT WE MUST FIND *CENTRAL CONTROL*...THE HEART OF IT ALL

WHAT ABOUT THE ROBOTS? SOME OF THEM COULD TEAR US TO PIECES!...

Q.272

AND AS THE INTRUDERS BEGIN TO EXPLORE THE VAST, MAZE-LIKE SOLAR STATION...

THE ROBOTS ARE MERELY AUTOMATONS, ONLY CAPABLE OF PERFORMING THEIR INDIVIDUAL FUNCTIONS! THEY WILL NOT HARM US...*UNLESS* WE GET IN THEIR WAY!

THE DANGER WILL COME WHEN WE FIND CENTRAL CONTROL! IT IS SUPERVISED BY AN ANDROID ... THE ONLY REASONING "BRAIN" IN THE WHOLE SYSTEM! *HE* WILL CERTAINLY REACT TO OUR PRESENCE!

I'M GLAD YOU KNOW SOMETHING ABOUT THIS PLACE, MELCHAR!

THAT'S FAIR ENOUGH... *HE* DOESN'T KNOW ABOUT *US* YET!

A FEW FACTS HAVE BEEN PUBLISHED ...BUT NOT ENOUGH! I KNOW THIS ANDROID EXISTS... HE IS CALLED *THE GUARDIAN*...BUT I DO NOT KNOW HIS PRECISE POWERS

Q.273

THE HOURS OF SEARCHING BECOME DAYS...

ANY FOOD TABLETS LEFT?... WE'VE BEEN EXPLORING THIS PLACE FOR TWO DAYS AND WE'RE STILL NO NEARER TO FINDING CONTROL CENTRE!

I FEAR THIS PLAN OF THE POWER HOUSE IS INACCURATE! OF COURSE, IT WAS DRAWN UP BY GUESSWORK FROM THE FEW SCRAPS OF AVAILABLE INFORMATION...

A PANEL OPENS IN THE GREY METAL WALL...

...BUT WE SHOULD BE *SOMEWHERE* NEAR...

YOU SEEK CONTROL CENTRE... YOU HAVE FOUND IT! *I AM THE GUARDIAN!*

Q.274

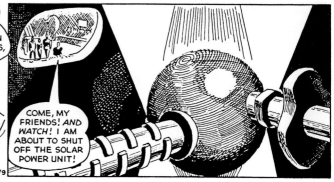

YOU SEE THE GREAT CORE OF SCANTHIUM IS SLOWLY MOVING OUT? WHEN IT IS WITHDRAWN FROM THE SPHERE, ALL POWER WILL CEASE TO RADIATE FROM THE OUTPUT ANTENNAE OF THE POWER-HOUSE...

...EVERY MACHINE ON THE PLANET WILL CONTINUE TO OPERATE ON STORED POWER FOR ABOUT TWELVE HOURS... AND THEN *STOP!*

I WONDER HOW QUICKLY CENTRAL GOVERNMENT WILL FIND OUT WHAT IS HAPPENING?

YE·E·S...WE MAY HAVE TO STAND A SIEGE OF EVERYTHING THEY CAN THROW AT US... UNTIL THE RUN-DOWN OF POWER IS COMPLETE!

Q. 280

THE WORLD GOVERNMENT OF URGON IS IN SESSION...A RARE EVENT! AND ATTENDING THE SESSION IS THE MASTER OF A DISTANT DOMAIN... *HAREK!*

IT'S *CRAZY*, SKALDOR! THE POWER-STATION HASN'T FAILED IN THREE CENTURIES! IT *CAN'T* FAIL!

FACE FACTS, HAREK! YOU FLEW IN YOURSELF BECAUSE YOUR ANDROIDS REPORTED THAT, TWO HOURS AGO, THE OUTPUT OF RADIATED POWER STOPPED COMPLETELY! THE SAME THING IS HAPPENING ALL OVER THE PLANET!...

THE ANDROIDS KNOW WHETHER THEY ARE GETTING ANY JUICE OR NOT!

THEN...THEY ARE OPERATING ON STORED POWER... WHICH WILL LAST FOR *LESS THAN HALF A DAY!*

Q. 281

LISTEN, YOU DOLLS! ISN'T THERE AN EMERGENCY VIEWING LINK WITH THE GUARDIAN OF THE POWER-HOUSE? I REMEMBER HEARING ABOUT IT

THERE IS, MASTER...

...BUT IT HAS NEVER BEEN NEEDED!

IT'S NEEDED *NOW!* GET THROUGH!

MELCHAR! LOOK! THAT SCREEN HAS LIT UP! THERE'S SOMEBODY ON IT!

IT'S SKALDOR... THE HEAD OF THE GOVERNMENT!

Q.282

THAT...THAT BIG ONE! HE'S AN *ALIEN!*

IT'S... *GARTH!* A CRITTUR I BROUGHT FROM SOME LITTLE OUT-BACK PLANET! B...BUT HE'S *DEAD!*

WHERE'S THE GUARDIAN? WHO *ARE* YOU? HOW DID YOU-?

I AM MELCHAR, OF *THE THINKERS!* AND THIS IS GARTH, FROM A PLANET CALLED EARTH

Q. 283

WITH TWO OTHERS, WE HAVE STOPPED THE OUTPUT OF ALL POWER ...BECAUSE WE BELIEVE IT TO BE THE ONLY WAY TO SAVE THIS CIVILISATION FROM COMPLETE DECAY!

THAT'S ONE THING... BUT AREN'T WE HOPING TO GET A FREE TRIP HOME OUT OF THIS, ROGAN?

THEY'RE MAD! *CRAZY!* THEY'RE GOING TO BRING EVERY MACHINE ON THE PLANET TO A *STANDSTILL!*

I OFFER YOU TERMS, SKALDOR... YOU MUST YIELD THE REINS OF GOVERNMENT TO *THE THINKERS*, UNDER KYRON...

Q.284

...OUR PLANS ARE READY! WE SHALL RADIATE LIMITED POWER TO CERTAIN TYPES OF MACHINE ...TO PREVENT CHAOS, BUT NOT ENOUGH TO SAVE MAN FROM HAVING TO WORK AND THINK AGAIN!

THEY WANT TO TURN THE WHOLE RACE INTO A BUNCH OF PRIMITIVES!... *THINKERS*, LIKE THEMSELVES!

WE'VE HEARD ENOUGH! SWITCH OFF!... HAREK, YOU STAY CLOSE BY *ME!* YOU SEEM TO KNOW MORE ABOUT THESE ALIENS THAN ANYONE ELSE!

GARTH

36

RUN LIKE HELL, ROGAN! MAKE FOR THE OTHER GRAV-SHAFT!

GARTH'S LEADING THEM AWAY FROM CONTROL CENTRE... BUT IT'LL BE AT LEAST *THREE HOURS* BEFORE THOSE ROBOTS ARE DUE TO RUN OUT OF JUICE!

THEY'RE USING STUN-GUNS, BRON... THEY WANT US *ALIVE* – AND I CAN GUESS WHY!

KEEP GOING, ROGAN! THEY CAN'T GET A GOOD SHOT AT US IN THIS WARREN OF A PLACE!

ROGAN STUMBLES AND FALLS...

LEAVE ME, GARTH! I...I CANNOT GO ON! *(GASP)*

WE'LL MAKE IT TOGETHER, ROGAN!

I'M NOT GOING TO FACE BRON WITH THE NEWS THAT I LEFT THE LITTLE 'UN BEHIND!

UHH!

YOU HAVE HIT THE SMALLER CREATURE... HE IS STUNNED...BUT THE OTHER GOES ON!

HE IS ENTERING A GRAV-SHAFT!

AHH... (GASP)

CLANG
CLICK

GARTH'S IN THE GRAV-SHAFT! BUT THOSE ROBOTS ARE RIGHT ON HIS HEELS!

GOING UP, ROGAN! THAT DOOR WON'T HOLD THEM FOR LONG!

THUNDER! HE'S *OUT*!

A SLENDER BEAM OF RADIANCE CUTS THROUGH THE LOCK OF THE GRAV-SHAFT DOOR IN A MATTER OF SECONDS...

GARTH SOARS UP THE TOWERING GRAV-SHAFT, AND A MOMENT LATER THE ROBO-WARRIORS BURST THROUGH IN PURSUIT...

THE SCENE IS RELAYED BY SCANNER TO THE CONTROL CENTRE...

HE'S REACHED THE TOP! BUT THEY'RE BOUND TO GET HIM... THEY'RE NOT MORE THAN FIVE SECONDS BEHIND!

WAIT! HE'S NOT JUST *RUNNING*! HE'S WORKING TO A PLAN! *LOOK*!

CLICK

AS GARTH CUTS THE POWER, THE ROBO-WARRIORS HURTLE DOWN THE THREE-HUNDRED-FOOT SHAFT TO DESTRUCTION...

CRASH

PHEW! (GASP) ...ONLY JUST MADE IT!

BUT ONE REMAINS! THE LEADER HAS REACHED SAFETY BY A SPLIT SECOND!

SUDDENLY MELCHAR'S VOICE RASPS URGENTLY FROM A HIDDEN SPEAKER!

LOOK OUT! GARTH! BEHIND YOU!

Q.295

...MUST HAVE REACHED THE TOP JUST AS I CUT THE POWER!...I'VE GOT TO GET HIM BEFORE HE CAN USE THAT GUN!

PSST

CRASH!

YOU'VE DONE IT, GARTH! YOU'VE DONE IT! THAT WAS THE LAST OF THEM!

WHAT'S HAPPENING? THOSE ROBOTS HAVE GOT BUILT-IN TRANSMITTERS! WHY HAVE THEY STOPPED REPORTING?

I AM RECEIVING NOTHING, MASTER...NOT EVEN THE NORMAL CARRIER-WAVE! IT CAN ONLY BE THAT THE ROBO-WARRIORS WHO SUCCEEDED IN ENTERING THE POWER-HOUSE HAVE BEEN DESTROYED...

Q.296

IN THE CONTROL CENTRE

THE LITTLE FELLOW'S GOING TO BE ALL RIGHT, ISN'T HE, MELCHAR?

YES...THE EFFECT OF THE STUN-GUN WILL WEAR OFF SOON... I WONDER WHAT SKALDOR WILL DO NOW!

HAS SKALDOR BEEN THROUGH ON THE VIEWER AGAIN?

NO...HE HAS NOT... I THINK WE HAVE WON, GARTH! WITH THE TUNNEL SEALED, THE POWER-HOUSE IS TRULY INVULNERABLE NOW! ITS POWER-BEAMS WILL THWART ANY ATTACK!

BUT IN SKALDOR'S OPERATIONS ROOM

WE'LL HAVE TO USE THE SECOND PLAN THE BIG BRAIN GAVE US!

EVERYTHING'S READY! WE'VE ONLY TO GIVE THE ORDER!

THEN GIVE IT, YOU FOOL! TIME'S RUNNING OUT! IF WE DON'T MAKE A BREAK-THROUGH IN TWO HOURS, THERE'LL BE NOTHING LEFT WORKING ON THE PLANET... EXCEPT HUMANS!

Q.297

WHAT'S THE MATTER, GARTH? WE CAN'T LOSE! THEY'LL NEVER BREACH THE POWER-HOUSE NOW ...LET ALONE WITH ONLY TWO HOURS TO DO IT!

MAYBE NOT...BUT LET'S WATCH THOSE ALARM LIGHTS AND KEEP AN EYE ON THINGS WITH THE SCANNER...

....I KNOW THIS PLACE IS INVULNERABLE...BUT I MISTRUST THAT WORD! WE FOUND A LOOP-HOLE, AND SO DID SKALDOR! THERE JUST MIGHT BE ANOTHER ONE!

Q.298

THE CRUCIAL MOMENT OF POWER-FAILURE WILL COME SUDDENLY, GARTH! WHEN THE FORCE-BEAMS THAT RING THE POWER-HOUSE FAIL, SO WILL ALL ROBOTS AND ANDROIDS ... EVERY WEAPON, EVERY MACHINE! OUR STRUGGLE WILL BE OVER!

I'M STILL UNEASY...

NO DOUBT YOUR ANCESTORS WHO BUILT THIS PLACE WERE VERY CLEVER...BUT CLEVER PEOPLE SOMETIMES OVERLOOK SIMPLE THINGS!

AN ALARM-LIGHT FLICKERS RED!

SOMETHING'S HAPPENING! DOWN ON THE LOWER LEVEL! QUICK...PICK IT UP ON THE SCANNER, MELCHAR!

Q.299

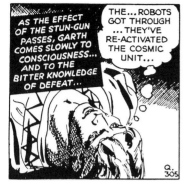

AS THE EFFECT OF THE STUN-GUN PASSES, GARTH COMES SLOWLY TO CONSCIOUSNESS... AND TO THE BITTER KNOWLEDGE OF DEFEAT...

THE... ROBOTS GOT THROUGH ...THEY'VE RE-ACTIVATED THE COSMIC UNIT...

GARTH! LOOK!

THE WARRIORS AND ROBO-SCIENTISTS STAND FROZEN AND UNMOVING...THE MYRIAD NEEDLES OF CENTRAL CONTROL NO LONGER FLICKER AGAINST THE GLOWING DIALS... THE WHOLE GREAT POWER-HOUSE LIES COLD AND DEAD!

WE... WE DID IT, ROGAN! THE STORED POWER RAN OUT BEFORE THEY COULD ACT!

LOOK, GARTH! THIS ONE WAS AT THE CONTROLS WHICH ACTIVATE THE COSMIC UNIT!

AND HE DIDN'T QUITE MAKE IT! WE WON BY SECONDS, ROGAN!

IN SKALDOR'S OPERATIONS-ROOM THERE IS TERROR AND DESPAIR!

NO POWER...NO POWER! WE'RE FINISHED, SKALDOR!... THE WHOLE WORLD IS FINISHED! WITH THE DOLLS DEAD, WE... WE CAN'T DO ANYTHING FOR OURSELVES!...

IT'S GROWING DARK NOW... AND WE DON'T EVEN KNOW HOW TO MAKE FIRE!

THE THINKERS WILL KNOW, HAREK... DO YOU REALISE THAT THE THINKERS ARE THE ONLY PEOPLE WHO CAN SAVE URGON NOW?

WAKE UP, MELCHAR! COME ON NOW... ON YOUR FEET!

WHAT... HAPPENED?

WE'VE WON, MELCHAR! EVERYTHING HAS COME TO A STOP! KYRON AND THE THINKERS WILL KNOW IT BY NOW!...

UHH

...THEIR ADVANCE PARTY WILL BE COMING IN SOON...ON THE BIG 'COPTER YOU ADAPTED TO OPERATE ON AN OLD-FASHIONED POWER UNIT OF ITS OWN!

AND THEN THE REAL WORK WILL BEGIN, MY FRIENDS! THERE IS A WHOLE WORLD TO BE SAVED!

THE FIRST GROUP OF "THINKERS," MADE UP OF THEIR SCIENTISTS, LANDS NEAR THE POWER-HOUSE...

AH! THERE'S SOLAN AND TARA!

IT'S GOOD TO SEE YOU! ALL'S QUIET IN THE CITY... I THINK THE POPULATION IS SUFFERING FROM SHOCK! THERE'S NO PANIC YET... BECAUSE THEY'RE TOO STUNNED...

BUT IT WON'T LAST! I'D SAY WE'VE GOT NO MORE THAN TWO DAYS TO GET OUR EMERGENCY PLANS INTO OPERATION!

THE "THINKERS" PREPARE TO TAKE OVER...

ARE ROGAN AND MELCHAR SAFE? WHAT ARE THEY DOING?

NOW LET ME GET THIS RIGHT...THEY'RE BUSY RE-PHASING THE OUTPUT SIDE OF THE POWER-HOUSE... WHATEVER THAT MIGHT MEAN!

IT MEANS THAT WHEN WE SWITCH ON AGAIN, NOTHING WILL PICK UP THE ALTERED POWER EXCEPT ROBOTS FITTED WITH THE NEW UNITS WE'VE BROUGHT IN!

BUT...WE HAVE SAD NEWS FOR YOU, GARTH... KYRON, OUR LEADER, IS ...DEAD!

GARTH

KYRON *DEAD*? BUT HOW...?

WE WILL TALK OF IT LATER... EVERY MOMENT COUNTS NOW!

ALL RIGHT... LET BRON LEAD YOUR MEN INTO THE POWER-HOUSE WHILE WE GO AND TALK WITH SKALDOR!

IN THE COUNCIL-HALL OF URGON'S CENTRAL CITY

HERE THEY COME...THE MAD DOGS!

YOU'D DO WELL TO FACE IT, HAREK...THE OLD WAYS ARE GONE! AND ONLY THE *THINKERS* HAVE THE KNOWLEDGE TO LEAD US IN WHAT LIES AHEAD...

HADN'T YOU BETTER CLEAR OUT? GARTH MAY NOT REMEMBER YOU *KINDLY* FOR TRYING TO KILL HIM!

GULP!

...IN ALL THIS, WE SEEK YOUR *CO-OPERATION*, SKALDOR

YOU SHALL HAVE IT... THE POWER-HOUSE WILL SOON BE WORKING AGAIN, YOU SAY?

YES...BUT THE POWER IT RADIATES WILL ONLY BE OF USE TO CERTAIN ROBOTS AND MACHINES IN WHICH WE ARE FITTING *NEW* PICK-UP UNITS!

WITHIN TWO DAYS WE SHALL HAVE A SPECIAL ANDROID ON EVERY DOMAIN THROUGHOUT THE PLANET... ANDROIDS PROCESSED TO ORGANISE FOR SURVIVAL!

THEY'LL BE *GIVING* ORDERS... NOT TAKING THEM!

HERE IS A COMPLETE SCHEDULE OF OUR PLANS FOR REORGANISING THE PLANET ONCE THE EARLY DAYS OF EMERGENCY ARE OVER

A WORLD WITHOUT ROBOTS, NO DOUBT?

NO! A *BALANCED* CULTURE, WHERE ROBOTS SERVE THEIR PURPOSE, BUT WHERE THE HUMAN SPIRIT LIVES AND BREATHES INSTEAD OF STAGNATING!

YOU MAY BE RIGHT (*SIGH*)...TELL ME, WHERE IS YOUR LEGENDARY LEADER OF *THE THINKERS*? WHERE IS KYRON?

KYRON...WAS... AN ANDROID...

WHAT?

IT IS TRUE, GARTH... *KYRON* WAS THE LAST AND MOST PERFECT MACHINE *THE MASTERS* EVER BUILT!

BUT HOW COULD AN *ANDROID* BE THE LEADER OF *THE THINKERS*?

HE TOLD US, JUST BEFORE THE POWER FINALLY FAILED... IT SEEMS THAT TOWARDS THE END OF THEIR TIME, *THE MASTERS* SAW WHAT THE FUTURE MIGHT HOLD...

HE TOLD US THIS...

...AND SO, MY CHILDREN, THEY BUILT *ME*... TO THWART THAT POSSIBLE FUTURE...TO ACT AS TEACHER, GUIDE AND LEADER TO THOSE FEW WHO WOULD STRIVE TO KEEP ALIVE THE TRUE SPIRIT OF MANKIND...

WORK GOES ON UNCEASINGLY UNTIL AT LAST ALL IS READY FOR THE RE-ACTIVATION OF THE COSMIC UNIT...

KYRON SHOULD HAVE SEEN THIS MOMENT!... IT'S STRANGE...I STILL CAN'T THINK OF HIM AS A *MACHINE*!

BUT WE CAN BRING HIM BACK TO LIFE AGAIN NOW, CAN'T WE?

HE COMMANDED US NOT TO, BRON...

WITH OUR VICTORY, HIS WORK WAS ENDED... HE COULD NOT OPERATE BEYOND THE PURPOSE FOR WHICH HE WAS MADE

JUST A MACHINE... BUT IT'S STILL LIKE LOSING AN OLD FRIEND

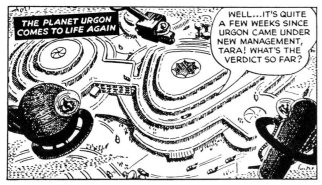

THE PLANET URGON COMES TO LIFE AGAIN

WELL...IT'S QUITE A FEW WEEKS SINCE URGON CAME UNDER NEW MANAGEMENT, TARA! WHAT'S THE VERDICT SO FAR?

WE'RE CERTAINLY THROUGH THE DANGER PERIOD! SOMEHOW WE'VE HELD OFF FAMINE AND PANIC, BOTH HERE IN CENTRAL CAPITAL AND IN ALL THE DOMAINS

NOW WE'RE BEGINNING TO BUILD A NEW CULTURE!

I'M GLAD SKALDOR HAD THE SENSE TO CO-OPERATE... HE'S BECOMING QUITE A THINKER

TARA! IS SOLAN HERE? I MUST SEE HIM AT ONCE!

SKALDOR REPORTS TO SOLAN, NEW CHIEF OF THE "THINKERS"

I'VE BEEN VISITING SOME OF THE DOMAINS, AS YOU WISHED ME TO, AND I'M NOT TOO HAPPY, SOLAN!

BUT WHY? THE PEOPLE ARE WORKING... TILLING GROUND, PLANTING CROPS, AND GENERALLY MAKING EACH DOMAIN SELF-SUPPORTING!

I KNOW! I'M SURPRISED AT WHAT'S BEEN DONE...AND I CAN'T SAY THERE'S BEEN ANY TROUBLE YET! BUT THERE ARE STRAWS IN THE WIND...

WHAT SORT OF TROUBLE IS BREWING, SKALDOR?

STRANGELY ENOUGH, YOU THINKERS ARE NOT UNPOPULAR! PEOPLE KNOW THAT WITHOUT YOU THEY COULD NOT SURVIVE...

BUT THEIR RESENTMENT AT BEING UNDER THE ORDERS OF THOSE SUPERVISING ANDROIDS YOU SENT OUT IS GROWING FIERCER EVERY DAY!

THAT'S WONDERFUL! JUST WHAT WE HOPED FOR! THE SOONER THEY WANT TO RUN THINGS FOR THEMSELVES, THE BETTER!

IT MEANS THEY'RE BECOMING MEN AT LAST, SKALDOR... THINKING MEN!

GASP!

THINGS ARE GOING BETTER THAN WE DARED HOPE!... IT SEEMS THAT THE SPIRIT OF MAN WAS NOT DEAD ON URGON...ONLY SLEEPING, GARTH!

WE HAVE MUCH TO THANK YOU FOR, MY FRIEND!

DON'T PUT IT TOO HIGH, SOLAN...THE MAIN REASON THAT BRON AND ROGAN AND I TURNED YOUR WORLD UPSIDE DOWN WAS BECAUSE THAT WAS THE ONLY WAY OF GETTING BACK TO OUR OWN WORLDS!

GOOD NEWS, GARTH!

MELCHAR HAS FINISHED FITTING NEW PICK-UP UNITS INTO A NUMBER OF SPACE-SHIPS!

WE CAN GO HOME, GARTH ...HOME!

TOMORROW!

THAT NIGHT, THERE IS A GREAT FEAST...

...SO IN A FEW HOURS WE SHALL PART, EH, LITTLE MAN? YOU AND I AND THAT GREAT EARTHMAN GARTH... (SIGH)...AFTER ALL OUR BATTLES, WE MUST GO OUR SEPARATE WAYS...

AGHH!...THIS WINE MAKES A MAN SAD...

Garth (2)

In 1971 there was an editorial decision taken to re-vamp the *'Garth'* strip and the artist chosen to do it was Frank Bellamy who had a very powerful style and had become well known because of his dynamic work on such strips as *'Dan Dare'* and *'Fraser of Africa'* in the famous *'Eagle'* magazine. Sadly, Bellamy died in 1976. The artwork on the strip was ably taken over by Martin Asbury who continued to draw it in an equally dynamic style until Garth's recent retirement right here in the '90's. The story that follows features the last of Frank Bellamy's work and the first Garth illustrations by Martin Asbury...

46

47

GARTH

GARTH

49

GARTH

52

GARTH

HAVE TO TRY TO PICK THEM OFF ONE BY ONE — THAT MEANS KEEPING THEM APART! WON'T BE EASY!

K 283

Garth sees his chance...

BAAYEE!

ONE DOWN — THREE TO GO! IF I CAN REACH THAT JUNGLE AND—

HE HAS KILLED GESTIS AND OCOLON — NOW WE KILL!

NO, THROW HIM OVER THE RIFT TO JOIN OCOLON

K 284

LET HIS BONES BLEACH BESIDE OCOLON'S!

NO, MY CHILDREN — HE IS MORE USE TO ME ALIVE!

Zetis, Lord of the Artemids...

THERE WAS A WOMAN WITH HIM, MASTER — WE COULD NOT FIND HER!

SHE IS SAFE! I HAVE BEEN WATCHING FROM THE TREES!

WHY DID YOU INVADE OUR LAND AND KILL TWO OF MY PEOPLE?

WE CAME HERE FOR A REASON! I KILLED ONLY IN SELF-DEFENCE!

K285

YOU WILL FIND THE WOMAN ON A LEDGE BELOW THE RIFT. BRING HER HERE!

AYE, MASTER

I SAW YOU FROM THE TREES! YOU HAVE COURAGE AND RESOURCE!

YOU ARE NOT OF THESE PEOPLE! ARE YOU A VOLTERRAN?

MY MOTHER WAS VOLTERRAN, MY FATHER WAS AN ARTEMID — BUT MAKE NO MISTAKE, STRANGER, I AM NO MISBRED BRUTE — I, ZETIS, RULE THESE PEOPLE THROUGH MY BRAIN!

K286

The Artemid returns with Athena...

LET ME GO, YOU GREAT ANTHROPOID!

THE WOMAN HAS SPIRIT — SHE IS BEAUTIFUL TOO! RELEASE HER, LITTLE BROTHER!

K287

SHE IS A CREATURE FAR ABOVE YOUR PUNY INTELLIGENCE

ZETIS, I'D BETTER TELL YOU WHY WE ARE HERE!

Garth explains his mission...

SO YOU WANT TO TAKE A **LIVE** ARTEMID BACK TO VOLTERRA FOR YOUR TESTS!

HE'LL COME TO NO HARM, I PROMISE!

AND IF YOU RESTORE THOSE FEEBLE VOLTERRAN MANIKINS TO VIRILITY, YOU ARE FREE TO RETURN TO EARTH.

THAT WAS THE DEAL, ZETIS.

IF THAT VOLTERRAN HAG MIRALDA CAN NAME A PRICE FOR YOUR LIBERTY, GARTH, SO CAN I! YOU CAN HAVE AN ARTEMID, BUT...

...ATHENA STAYS HERE AS MY CONSORT!

NOT ON YOUR LIFE! ATHENA RETURNS TO EARTH WITH ME!

K288

YOU ARE IN NO POSITION TO ARGUE, EARTHMAN — BRING THEM TO THE CAMP, LITTLE BROTHERS!

DON'T TRY TO ESCAPE, GARTH! THE SWAMP IS OUR NATURAL DEFENCE — ONLY ARTEMIDS CAN CROSS IT SAFELY!

ONCE THEY GET US DEEP INTO THEIR TERRITORY WE'RE TRAPPED! WE'LL HAVE TO MAKE OUR ESCAPE BID SOON, ATHENA!

K289

AN OLDER CIVILISATION ONCE LIVED HERE WITH STYLE AND CULTURE — BUT THEY GREW LAZY! THE ARTEMIDS DID THE REST!

K290

HAVE YOU DECIDED YET, ATHENA? DO YOU STAY WITH ME AND LET GARTH RETURN WITH HIS ARTEMID?

I GO WITH GARTH!

THEN I'LL MAKE YOU A PROPOSITION, EARTHMAN — YOU SHALL HAVE YOUR ARTEMID AND GO BACK WITH ATHENA — BUT THERE ARE CONDITIONS...

WHAT ARE YOUR CONDITIONS, ZETIS?

QUITE SIMPLE FOR A MAN OF YOUR COURAGE AND STRENGTH

THIS IS KOTLIK — THE BEST OF MY TRAINED FIGHTING MEN! VANQUISH HIM IN COMBAT AND YOU CAN TAKE HIM!

NO, GARTH! IT'S A TRICK!

K291

ATHENA MAY BE RIGHT! WHAT'S ON YOUR MIND, ZETIS?

KOTLIK KNOWS ONLY ONE WAY TO FIGHT — TO THE DEATH! THAT IS THE CHANCE YOU HAVE TO TAKE!

I TAKE YOUR CHALLENGE, ZETIS! IF I BEAT YOUR MAN HE COMES BACK TO VOLTERRA WITH ATHENA AND ME!

AGREED!

WHEN THIS IS OVER, ATHENA, YOU WILL SEE MANY CONTESTS LIKE THIS — AS MY CONSORT

I DOUBT IT, ZETIS! SOMEHOW YOU HAVE GAINED ASCENDANCY OVER THESE BRUTES — WHAT HAPPENS WHEN THEY SEE THROUGH YOUR TRICKS?

WATCH YOUR MAN DIE, WOMAN!

K292

GARTH

56

GARTH

59

Andy Capp

The Mirror's most famous cartoon character first appeared in print in just the Northern edition of the Mirror back in August 1957 as a single panel cartoon. His creator, cartoonist Reg Smythe, had started life 40 years previously in Hartlepool during one of the North's many periods of unemployment. Reg left school at 14, worked as a delivery boy, was on the dole, joined the army and got caught up, like everyone else, in a little skirmish called World War Two.

After the war Reg moved down to London and worked for the Post Office. While there he tried his hand at cartooning and after a few false starts he started to sell gag cartoons to various periodicals. Like many cartoonists, Reg worked on his drawings after he had finished his 'day job'. Eventually he started getting his cartoons into the *'Laughter'* column in the Daily Mirror. After a while Reg was asked to take over a little feature called *'Laughter at Work'* which appeared every day. Having settled into this job he took a holiday and went back to Hartlepool to visit his mother. He had only been gone a couple of days when he received a telegram from the cartoon editor asking him to think up a new cartoon that would appeal to Northern readers to help in a circulation drive in that area. On the journey back to London, Reg thought up the *'Andy Capp'* character and the rest, as they say, is history. After Andy appeared in the Northern edition he soon proved popular enough to be published in the South as well. Since then, his adventures have been expanded into strip cartoon form and appear all over the world. Sadly, Reg died in June 1998 but his memory and his humour will live on with Andy and Florrie.

An example of Smythe's early
'Laughter at Work' cartoon (1954).

" No, not that one lass, I'm on 'oliday! "

Andy's first appearance.
August 5th., 1957.

"Remember now,
I don't want to be
invited back again—
so just be yourself."

"Let's eat out tonight, Florrie."

"*No thanks, I'm not comin' with yer this time—*
yer can blow the ball up yerself!"

ANDY CAPP

64

-AND STAY OUT! YOU'RE NOT A MEMBER!

'OW COME A MISERABLE DEVIL LIKE YOU EVER GOT A JOB AS A DOORMAN?!!

I LIKE MEETIN' PEOPLE

WONDER IF SHE GOT THAT LOAN FOR ME?

ANY LUCK, PET?

THAT'S MY MUM-IN-LAW — ALWAYS LENDS ME ENOUGH TO TIDE ME UNDER

TCH~!

COULD YOU DO SOMETHIN' ABOUT THE NOISE, ANDY?

SORRY, TED, NOT A THING. IF I LIE SHE RANTS AN' RAVES, AN' IF I TELL THE TRUTH SHE GOES BERSERK

HURRY UP WI' THAT NEWSPAPER. I WANT TO READ MY STARS

I'LL READ THEM FOR YOU. GEMINI... ...YOU'RE GOIN' TO BE LEFT SOME MONEY BY AN UNKNOWN AUNT—

UNKNOWN AUNT? I DON'T KNOW OF ANY UNKNOWN AUNT—!

GIVE ME STRENGTH

BE BACK IN A MINUTE, JACKIE, I'M JUST GOIN' TO PICK UP MY BLIND DATE—

ARE YOU JULIE?

ARE YOU ANDY? YES—

NO

I WISH THE GOVERNMENT WOULD DO SOMETHIN' ABOUT UNEMPLOYMENT

THAT'S THREE DAYS IN A ROW I HAVEN'T BEEN ABLE TO GET ON THE POOL TABLE AT LUNCHTIME!

Q226

AN' YOU THINK YOU'VE GOT PROBLEMS

PAY DAY, PET

Q227

A KIND OF MUGGING

I DID IT AGAIN, FLO! SCORED THE WINNIN' GOAL FROM A PENALTY IN THE VERY LAST MINUTE

Q228

NO DOUBT ABOUT IT— SOMEBODY UP THERE LIKES ME

I'M NOT SO SURE ABOUT SOME OF US DOWN 'ERE, MATE!

YOU'LL BE BACK

COO! COO! COO! COO!

OH, NO I WON'T. I'LL SURVIVE

COO! COO!

Q292

I'VE GOT FRIENDS, Y'KNOW!

GRANTED—

BUT 'AVE YOU EVER TRIED TO BORROW MONEY FROM A PIGEON?

ALWAYS SHORT, EH, FLO?

ALWAYS, RUBE. AN' 'E'S EVEN SHORTER ON THANKS

Q295

I SHOULD THINK SO

I MET MUM IN THE MARKET, PET, AND GUESS WHAT — SHE WON THE JACKPOT AT BINGO LAST NIGHT!

T7

GOOD FOR HER. I AM PLEASED — I REALLY MEAN THAT

TRULY?

TRULY —

THE MORE THEY HAVE THE LESS YOU SEE OF 'EM

SAY SOMETHING

U115

IF MY MOTHER ASKS ME WHY I MARRIED YOU IN THE FIRST PLACE — WHAT SHOULD I TELL HER ?!!

LOVELY NIGHT, FLO

GORGEOUS. THE MOON SO BLUE AND THE STARS SO BRIGHT —

ON NIGHTS LIKE THIS I LOOK UP AT THE SKY AND PONDER ON THE MYSTERIES OF THE UNIVERSE —

U118

AND WHETHER TO GIVE HIS SUPPER TO THE DOG NEXT DOOR OR THROW IT IN HIS FACE

ALL RIGHT, KEEP YOUR MONEY — !

U119

I'M NOT GOING TO GROVEL — I'VE GOT MY PRIDE, Y'KNOW!

HUH! IT SEEMS TO ME THE PEOPLE WITH THE MOST PRIDE ARE THE ONES WITH THE LEAST TO BE PROUD OF

DID YOU HEAR THAT? SHE'S TALKING TO A LAD WHO CAN SINK TWELVE PINTS AND STILL FIND HIS WAY HOME

TCH, THE TIME! SHE'LL BLOW HER TOP... WELL, HERE GOES —

I'M SORRY, PET. IT'S LIKE THIS —

THAT'S ALL RIGHT, PET —

T263

I'VE JUST COME IN MYSELF. RUBE AND ME —

THERE'S ABSOLUTELY NO EXCUSE FOR COMING IN AT THIS TIME OF NIGHT — !!

Romeo Brown

'Romeo Brown' was a light hearted, tongue-in-cheek private detective story with a particular focus on amazingly attractive girl characters. The strip started in 1954 and was drawn by Dutch artist Alfred Mazure. When 'Maz' left to work elsewhere in 1957, the strip was taken over by talented artist, Jim Holdaway. It didn't take long for Jim to make the strip his own and his glamourous girls brightened up many a male reader's breakfast read! The strip was written by Peter O'Donnell during the time that it was illustrated by Holdaway and after 'Romeo Brown' finished in 1962, the two of them created another famous adventure strip, 'Modesty Blaise'. Sadly, Jim Holdaway died in 1970 but as a nice reminder of his talented work, here are two 'Romeo Brown' adventures from 1961...

ROMEO BROWN

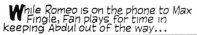

ROMEO BROWN

Through Fan's marriage bureau, Abdul's two sisters have flown off to Kaff as prospective brides of the sheik—not knowing that he is a hereditary enemy of the family...

MIZ PEACH!
THUMP!

—ALL IS CHATTERS AND TEA-DRINK! BUT IS NOT DETECTINGS MINE ZISTERS!

NOW, NOW, ABDUL – YOU CAN RELY ON MR. BROWN!

IF ABDUL LEARNS THE TRUTH, HE'LL GO POTTY, FAN!

NEVER MIND 'IM... IT'S BAHLI AN' JAHLI WHAT'S IN DEAD TROUBLE! WE GOTTER GET 'EM BACK SAFE AN' SOUND!

YOU'LL HAVE TO TAKE ABDUL OFF OUR HANDS WHILE WE GET AIRBORNE FOR KAFF!

WE? YOU MEAN – YOU AN' THAT MISS PEACH? WELL, 'OW VERY ROMANTIC!

IT'S NOT LIKE THAT, FAN!

IT WOULD BE IF YOU 'AD THE SAY-SO,! OR IF IT WAS ME GOIN' WITH YOU AN' I 'AD THE SAY-SO,! (SIGH)...

AH, WELL, THAT'S LIFE...

I S'POSE I'D BETTER GET BUSY ON ALADDIN 'ERE, IF YOU WANT 'IM OUT OF YOUR 'AIR FOR A BIT

MR. BROWN'S DECIDED WE'LL SPLIT UP AN' START TALKIN' TO ALL THE TAXI-DRIVERS 'OO MIGHT 'AVE CARRIED YOUR SISTERS, SEE?

HA! NOW WE WILL DID SOMETHINGS AT LAST!

COME ON, THEN, ABDUL – I'LL START YOU OFF WITH THE CAB-RANK AT EUSTON

THAT'LL KEEP 'IM BUSY WHILE ROMEO AN' MISS PERISHIN' PEACH GET AIRBORNE...!

THANKS, FAN – YOU'RE A MARVEL AT FIXING THINGS

OH, SHUT UP, SOPPY... AN'-AN' DO TAKE CARE OF YOURSELF IN KAFF, LOVE...

The hot sun looks down upon the desert caravan-trail leading to Kaff – and two travellers move steadily on their way...

I KNEW IT..! I KNEW IT FROM THE START!

BUT WE COULDN'T LAND AT KAFF ITSELF, MISS PEACH – THAT WOULD HAVE BEEN ASKING FOR TROUBLE! AND WE HAD TO ARRIVE SUITABLY DISGUISED...

GETTING BAHLI AND JAHLI AWAY FROM THE SHEIK IS GOING TO BE A REAL UNDERCOVER JOB, YOU KNOW

I'M CERTAINLY UNDER-COVERED, MR. BROWN! OH, I JUST KNEW I'D LOSE MY CLOTHES, WORKING WITH YOU!

As Romeo and Miss Peach sight the town of Kaff where the Sheik's Palace stands...

JUST WHO ARE WE SUPPOSED TO BE?

WELL... I CAN PASS AS A SORT OF MINOR SHEIK, AND YOU CAN BE...

I WILL NOT POSE AS YOUR WIFE, MR. BROWN!

OH GOLLY I WOULDN'T DREAM OF SUCH A THING MISS PEACH!

DON'T WORRY – I'LL PASS YOU OFF AS MY NUMBER ONE CONCUBINE

OH!

77

80

RATHER A PITY ABOUT MR. BROWN AND HIS TWO YOUNG LADIES – – BUT HEIGH-HO...THE LAW IS THE LAW!

HAVE YOU ORGANISED THE POTS, THE OIL AND THE HEATING ARRANGEMENTS, ALI?

YEA, MASTER – BUT I HAVE HERE A MESSAGE FROM THE PRISONERS

CRUMBS, I HOPE YOUR IDEA WORKS, FAN!

WE'LL SOON KNOW, MR. BROWN – HERE COMES THE VIZIER!

NOW LOOK 'ERE, O VIZIER! AGES AGO THERE WAS A GEEZER 'OO WAS GOING TO 'AVE A YOUNG LADY DONE IN...

...BUT 'E DI'N'T BECAUSE SHE KEP' 'IM AMUSED WITH STORIES AN' SUCHLIKE FOR A THOUSAND AND ONE NIGHTS!

AHH! THE CASE OF SCHEHERAZADE, H'M? IT FORMS PART OF OUR ANCIENT LAW!

GOOD! THEN FOR AS LONG AS WE ALL KEEP YOU AMUSED EVERY NIGHT, YOU CAN'T 'AVE US BOILED IN OIL!

GRACIOUS ME! I THINK YOU ARE RIGHT, MY DEAR!

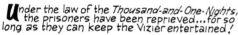

Under the law of the *Thousand-and-One-Nights*, the prisoners have been reprieved...for so long as they can keep the Vizier entertained!

PHEW! AT LEAST WE'VE GOT A CHANCE TO ESCAPE NOW!

AND THEN WE MUST HAVE ANOTHER TRY TO RESCUE BAHLI AND JAHLI FROM THE SHEIK – THAT'S WHAT WE CAME FOR!

FIRST THING IS TO PUT ON A GOOD SHOW FOR THAT VIZIER BLOKE TONIGHT! 'ERE, GET STEADIED UP AN' THEN WE'LL START REHEARSING, LOVE!

I KNOW A CORKING JOKE – IF I CAN REMEMBER IT...

The first of the *Thousand-and-One-Nights* entertainment...

I'LL TELL MY JOKE TO PUT HIM IN A GOOD MOOD, AND THEN I'LL INTRODUCE YOUR 'BUTTERFLY DANCE'

YOU BETTER OPEN THEM WINGS AN' STICK A SMILE ON THAT DISH OF YOURS, MISS PEACH! YOU'RE S'POSED TO BE A DANCIN' BUTTERFLY – NOT A CREEPIN' CATERPILLAR!

GOOD EVENING, AND THANK YOU, FANS!! A VERY FUNNY THING HAPPENED ON MY WAY THROUGH THE HAREM TODAY... (YUK-YUK)...

Romeo the comic..(?)

...SO THE OTHER GIRL SAID (YUK-YUK!) – SHE SAID – ER...

UM-AH...? (GULP)... OH, CRIKEY – I'VE FORGOTTEN THE PUNCH-LINE!

H'MM!... YOUR LIVES DEPEND ON YOUR AMUSING ME, MR. BROWN – SO IF I SHOULD DROP OFF TO SLEEP, YOU WILL ALL BE (YAWN) – DOOMED I FEAR...

OH DEAR!

PSST! ANNOUNCE OUR BUTTERFLY DANCE – QUICK, LOVE!

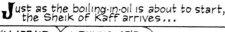

86

ROMEO BROWN

ROMEO BROWN

97

101

Romeo and Fan leave Mizzen Bay together...

I STILL DON'T GET IT, FAN...

WHAT MADE CINDY **REALISE** THAT SHE WAS CRACKERS ABOUT BRUCE? I MEAN, SOMETHING MUST HAVE **HAPPENED** TO MAKE HER SEE IT SO SUDDENLY!

'COURSE IT DID, LOVE! ER... PULL IN FOR A MINUTE, AN' I'LL TELL YOU!

IT WAS **ME** 'OO MADE CINDY REALISE SHE LOVED BRUCE! 'COS WHEN 'E **KIDNAPPED** 'ER AN' BROUGHT 'ER TO DOG ISLAND, I **FLUNG** MESELF IN 'IS ARMS—

— LIKE THIS! THEN I KISSED 'IM LIKE **THIS** AN' **THIS** AN' **THIS**! AN' IN TWO TICKS SHE WAS FIT TO SCRATCH ME EYES OUT!

C-CRUMBS! (GASP)—ER... WE'D BETTER GET ON, FAN!

I THOUGHT WE **WERE**! (SIGH)... STILL, I'LL RUN OVER IT AGAIN LATER, WHEN WE GOT MORE **TIME**, LOVE...

Useless Eustace

'Useless Eustace', the little 'everyman' character with the extremely round and extremely bald head, was drawn every day for around 40 years by Jack Greenall, a cartoonist whose work had appeared in practically all of the leading magazines of his day. Eustace made his debut in January 1935 and continued under Greenall's supervision until April 1974. The single panel feature was continued by a different artist in a re-vamped style until 1985 but it is the original version of 'Useless Eustace' by Jack Greenall that we must record here. Our selection comes from both the war years and the sixties...

"BUT DASH IT, SIR, ITS THE LEAST WE CAN DO! — THE WIFE'S VOLUNTEERED FOR WAR WORK — //"

"GOT A BIT OF COAL IN YOUR EYE? GOOD FOR YOU, WALTER! — EVERY LITTLE HELPS, NOW IT'S RATIONED //"

"SH-H-H! — I PURPOSELY LEFT THE FRONT DOOR WIDE OPEN, OFFICER! — THE WIFE KEEPS THREATENING TO WALK OUT ON ME — //"

"SAY, CHUM! WOULD YOU MIND TELLING GEORGE AND ALBERT THEIR OLD PAL EUSTACE IS HERE?!!"

"— AND NOW THE ST. LOUIS BLUES! PLAYED IN STRICT SWING TEMPO ——//"

"COURSE THE LETTUCE IS CLEAN! WASHED IT MYSELF THOROUGHLY, I DID! — WITH GOOD SOAP AND WATER—//"

"FED UP? BLIMEY! WOULDN'T YOU BE FED UP IF YOU'D JUST POSTED YOURSELF YOUR FINAL DEMAND — ?!!"

"EARLY PEAS INDEED! LOOK! MID-DAY! AND NOT ONE OF THE BLIGHTERS ARE EVEN UP YET — !! "

"I'M TAKING NO CHANCES! — IN FIVE MINUTES FROM NOW IT'LL BE THE RUSH HOUR —!! "

"COURSE IT'S FRESH! — WELL IT WAS BEFORE YOU STARTED ARGUING ABOUT THE PRICE, LADY —!! "

"WELL! SO-LONG, TED! — KEEP YOUR CHIN UP —!! "

" FRANKLY I SEE NOTHING WONDERFUL IN HIM BEING 96 YEARS OLD! – BLIMEY! LOOK AT THE TIME ITS TAKEN HIM TO DO IT —!! "

"H'M! BETTER CUT OUT YOUR HEALTH EXERCISES FOR A WHILE! — THEY'RE WEARING YOU DOWN !!"

"WELL, VICAR! I COULD GIVE THE BRIDE AWAY! BUT WE AGREED TO LET BYGONES BE BYGONES —!!"

"BLIMEY! IT WOULDN'T HURT YOU TO LEND ME SLINGSBY'S MOWER! –AFTER ALL, I WAS DECENT ENOUGH TO LEND YOU RAMSBOTTOM'S RAKE !!"

"I'M AFRAID THIS ISN'T MUCH FUN FOR YOU, WINNIE, DEAR //"

"MY 'USBAND 'ERE WISHES TO COMPLAIN ABOUT THE NOISE!"

"AS A LAST RESORT THEY GOT 'IM A JOB IN A GLUE FACTORY, BUT 'E COULDN'T EVEN STICK TO THAT //"

"GAFFER! - 'E'S KNOCKIN' OFF BEFORE TIME AGAIN"

"FRANKLY, MATE, YOU'VE BEEN FLOGGIN' TEN DEAD 'ORSES //"

105

"IT'S BEEN TRIED, MATE !"

"I'M WARNIN' YOU TWO — IF I CATCH YOU AGAIN I'M GOIN' TO SELL THAT SETTEE !"

" OL' EUSTACE 'AS BIN PROMISED ONE OF 'EM !"

" I SAID, 'AVE YOU 'EARD THE LATEST WHISPER GOIN' AROUND THE SITE ?!"

USELESS EUSTACE

"'E'S TEACHIN' 'IM OBEDIENCE, MUM — CAN 'E BRING 'IM IN TO WATCH DAD ?!"

"SHOULDN'T YOU BE WRITIN' ALL THIS DOWN, EUSTACE ?!"

"I'VE ONLY GOT A NET INCOME —— I'M IN THE TRAWLIN' BUSINESS !"

"ME WIFE WANTS TO KISS ME OVER THE PHONE — TAKE THE MESSAGE — I'LL GET IT FROM YOU LATER !"

"SHE'S EXPECTIN' A 'APPY EVENT — 'E WON'T LET 'ER CARRY A THING !"

Calamity Gulch

Cartoonist Jack Clayton had many of his single 'gag' cartoons published in the Mirror's cartoon column and the subject matter of his jokes quite regularly featured cowboys and indians in the old wild west. He used the theme often enough to prompt him to create a daily dose of crazy cowboy capers which he set in the little western town of *Calamity Gulch*. In fact, the name of this town was also used as the title of his cartoon feature which made it's debut on 6th June, 1960. Let's join Miss Lucy and all the rest of those wild and woolly westerners for a few laughs-on-the-range.

"Would you move back slightly, Miss Lucy Belle?"

"Yup, Miss Lucy! My ole dawg comes in right handy fer washin' up the crockery."

"The Injuns are havin' a massacre? WHERE?"

"How did yuh git to be nicknamed 'Lucky'?"

"All right, somebody get Tiny Wolf there on course."

"Does this mean yo're gonna gimme trouble, McGinty?"

109

"What in 'tarnation can this here R.S.P.C.A. outfit wanta see me fer?"

"I reckon a little thing like no tracks don't worry the Spittoon Valley Express!"

"Next stop Calamity Gulch—next stop Calamity Gulch"

"Tumbleweed— I've had enough of you rushin' in here shoutin' 'Gold' jest so you can git a place at the bar!"

"Yep—it sure took a long time fer law to be established in Calamity Gulch."

"Go ahead—laugh yer head off—YOU don't have to cart the big, fat barrel of lard home!"

"Miss Lucy never calls ME 'Dreamboat'!"

"Elastic broke?"

"This place is gettin' to be a proper ghost-town!"

"Sheriff—the boys wuz wonderin' ef you would be so kind as to grant the saloon an extension tonight?"

111

"I thought it was about time the team from the Silver Dollar played us a return match!"

"Me still say top one look like Howling Wolf!"

"Ah reckon he's had enough, Tony"

Scorer

Sports strips have been popular in boy's comics over the years but never really caught on in newspapers. However, this all changed in 1989 when a new strip made it's debut amongst the pages of the Mirror's sports section. That strip was called 'Scorer', written by Barry Tomlinson and drawn by Barry Mitchell. The artwork was later taken over by John Gillatt.

The storylines focus on the lives and careers of Dave 'Scorer' Storry and his Tolcaster F.C. team-mates. The series proved so popular with a wider audience than just football fans, that it earned itself a place on the regular strip cartoon page. Our choice of story for this volume is from 1994 and shows that the action can get pretty hot both on and off the pitch for Dave Storry...

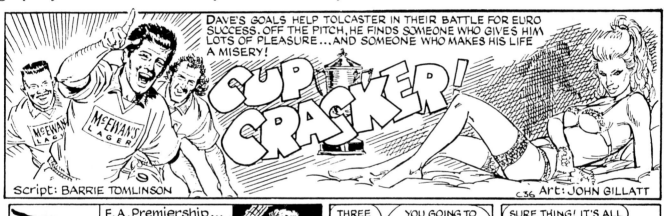

LOOKS AS IF DAVE'S A FAST MOVER AS USUAL!

HE DIDN'T HAVE TO DO A THING. SHE GRABBED HIM!

GILLATT & TOMLINSON

PHEW, YOU DON'T HANG ABOUT, DO YOU?

I'M AN AIR HOSTESS. I'M NEVER IN ONE PLACE LONG ENOUGH TO BE CONVENTIONAL!

I HEAR YOU'VE GOT A MEGA HOUSE. WHY NOT SHOW IT TO ME...NOW!

I DIDN'T WANT TO DANCE ANYWAY!

SO YOU WANT TO SEE ME HOUSE...

LATER, DAVE... FIRST THINGS FIRST!

SHOW ME WHY YOU'RE CALLED 'SCORER'!

GULP!

GILLATT & TOMLINSON

I'M GLAD YOU ARRIVED PREPARED!

A GIRL HAS TO TAKE PRECAUTIONS, THESE DAYS!

I GO TAKE A SHOWER THEN WE MAKE LOVE AGAIN!

I'VE GOT A MATCH TOMORROW!

THIS IS CRAZY...I DON'T EVEN KNOW YOUR NAME OR WHERE YOU'RE FROM!

I AM FROM DENMARK. I'M ULRIKA!

I'M FROM TOLCASTER. I'M OVER THE MOON!

GILLATT & TOMLINSON

HURRY UP, STORRY... YE'RE LATE!

SORRY, BOSS... LOOK AT THAT SILLY GRIN ON HIS FACE!

I RECOGNISE THAT LOOK, LADDIE...YE'VE GOT YESELF A NEW LASSIE! I HOPE YE'VE NOT BEEN OVERDOING IT!

GILLATT & TOMLINSON

NO WAY, BOSS MAN...

ZZZZZZ!

YE'D BETTER BE EXTRA SHARP TODAY, STORRY. DOZING OFF IN THE DRESSING ROOM IS NO' A HABIT I LIKE.

JUST KIDDING, BOSS!

YOU SURE YOU'RE OK

QUIT WORRYING. I'M GOING TO PLAY A BELTER. ULRIKA IS WATCHING...

...I'VE IMPRESSED HER OFF THE PITCH NOW I'VE GOT TO DO THE SAME WITH MY BOOTS ON!

GILLATT & TOMLINSON

SCORER

115

SCORER

Cup-Winners' Cup...

WHAT A SHOT BY LES HARKER!

CORNER TO TOLCASTER!

WEGGLE AT THE NEAR POST...

DAVE STORRY'S RACING IN...

DAVE GOT A BOOT ON THE HEAD

THAT LOOKS A BAD ONE!

UUURGH!

HE'S FLAT OUT!

I DON'T LIKE THE LOOK OF THIS. I'M TAKING HIM OFF!

Dave's world had disappeared into inky blackness...

Until...

I THINK HE'S COMING ROUND...

ABOUT TIME. ARE YE ALL RIGHT, LADDIE?

THE MATCH... I'VE GOT TO GET BACK TO THE MATCH!

IT'S ALL OVER, LADDIE!

YOU GOT YOURSELF KNOCKED OUT!

WHO WON?

IT WAS A NIL-NIL DRAW.

TAKE IT EASY, MR STORRY!

THIS IS DOCTOR SVENSON...

YOU RECEIVED A NASTY KNOCK. I THINK PERHAPS YOU SHOULD GO TO HOSPITAL FOR PRECAUTIONARY CHECKS!

I'M FINE. I CAN'T MISS THE FLIGHT BACK TO TOLCASTER. I'VE GOT A HOT DATE!

DAVE, I WAS SO WORRIED WHEN I SAW YOU KNOCKED UNCONSCIOUS!

LUCKY IT WAS ONLY MY HEAD THAT GOT BASHED!

THE BOSS INSISTED ON A HOSPITAL CHECK... BUT THEY GAVE ME THE ALL-CLEAR. NOW I JUST WANT TO RELAX.

I WILL MAKE YOU FORGET THE BRUISE ON YOUR HEAD!

I BET YOU WILL!

WHAT THE--?

WH-WHO WOULD THROW A BRICK THROUGH YOUR WINDOW?

THAT'S WHAT I'M ABOUT TO FIND OUT!

117

SCORER

119

SCORER

SCORER

127